Up, Up and Away

NORTH LONDON

Edited by Emma Marsden

First published in Great Britain in 2000 by
YOUNG WRITERS
Remus House,
Coltsfoot Drive,
Woodston,
Peterborough, PE2 9JX
Telephone (01733) 890066

HB ISBN 0 75432 086 3
SB ISBN 0 75432 087 1

FOREWORD

This year, the Young Writers' Up, Up & Away competition proudly presents a showcase of the best poetic talent from over 70,000 up-and-coming writers nationwide.

Successful in continuing our aim of promoting writing and creativity in children, our regional anthologies give a vivid insight into the thoughts, emotions and experiences of today's younger generation, displaying their inventive writing in its originality.

The thought, effort, imagination and hard work put into each poem impressed us all and again the task of editing proved challenging due to the quality of entries received, but was nevertheless enjoyable. We hope you are as pleased as we are with the final selection and that you continue to enjoy *Up, Up & Away North London* for many years to come.

CONTENTS

Michelle T Pereira	68
Tushar A Gadhia	69
Jasmine Anderson	70
Marzban Kapadia	70
Nathan Alex Asher	71
Aimee Louise Rogers	71

Muswell Hill Junior School

Jessie Kochan	72
Ella Bruce	72
Aimee Mackenzie	72
Mirella Louise Wilson	73
Harry Wilson	73
Clara Baldock	74
Amalia Randolph	74
Georgina Stevens	75
Emily Haynes	75
Matthew Fallon	76
Rasheeda Gafur	76
Hannah Baldock	77
Candice Desmuruis	77
Louis Marsh	78
Caspar Sonnet	78
Bella Travers	79
Madeleine Wickers	79
Joe Bourne	80
Tillie Holt	80
Louis Schamroth-Green	80
Rachel Stanigar	81
Eve Katherine Houghton	81
Alexia Argyrou	82
Kristina Goggin	82
Lois Bond	83
Elizabeth Donker-Curtius	83
Jess Thompson	84
Joe Beveridge	85

David Omoregie	85
Phoebe Fullbrook	86
Isabelle Aron	86
Michael Simpson	87
Joe Grant	87
Alexa Lawrence	88
Ben Lopez	88
Avi Walerius	89
Yoni Pakleppa	89
Niamh Mealey	90
Freddie Duffy	90
Sam Barrett Binney	91
Max Abse	92
Jason Bond	93
Janine L Houston	94
Akash Singh	94
Kairos Pakleppa	95

Norfolk House School

Dawn Duhaney	95
Ben Kustow	96
Gemma Mehmed	96
George Surtees	97
Anna Bootle	97
Afua Kokayi	98
Nicole Stennett	99

Osidge School

Sarah Grindall	100
Daniel Bezani	100
Kyri Neophytou	101
Vaishali Bhojani	101
Zarrin Ansari	102
Sean Shields	102
Danielle Davari	103
Alex Christodoulou	104

St Ignatius RC Primary School

St MartinOf Porres RC Primary School

Sean Parsons	156
Bobo Ahmed	157
Kathryn O'Donoghue	157
Ben Pugh	158
Frank Robinson	158
Imogen Massey	159
Natalie O'Brien	159
Antony Aguirre	160
Luke McGowan	160
Christina Paul	161
Joshua Baptiste	161
Elizabeth Camara	162
Carl Bleach	162
Emma Holtom	163
Daniel Rassaby	164
Sean Hamill	165
Sean Daly	165
Sinead Whitney	166
Christina Donellan	166
Danielle O'Neill	167

The Poems

THE BEACH

The beach is fun to play on,
It could never make its waves stop coming in.
The waves are always reflecting in the sun,
They could never reflect back onto the sun.
The people on the beach always have a nice suntan,
But could never stop drinking from a cold can.
The people playing beach ball,
Could never stop making a call.
The waves that come into the tide,
Could never be so wide.
The children that are playing,
Could never stop paying.
The adults who are talking,
Could never stop walking.
The people reading books,
Could be crooks!
The people who are parking,
Have dogs that never stop barking.
People's mobile phones kept on ringing,
But all I could hear was other people singing!

Carmen Ko (10)

UNICORN

If I could be reincarnated
(and who knows I might have been already)
then I'd like to return as a unicorn,
fast and enchanted.
Plunging down to Earth from my mystical
existence, then no one would take my
shimmering blood.

Marvin Bell (11)
Angel Primary School

UNICORN

If I could be reincarnated
(And who knows, I might have been already)
Then I'd like to return as a unicorn,
Graceful and enchanting.

Plummeting down to Earth
From my fluffy pillow.
Flying gracefully everywhere I go,
Meeting people all over the world.

And finally, I would love to be a unicorn
So my horn like a sparkling icicle
Will attract everyone
I see.

If I could be reincarnated
(And who knows, I might have been already)
Then I'd like return as a unicorn,
Graceful and enchanting.

Marie-Louise Mensah (11)
Angel Primary School

PAINTED PICTURE

Sleek, silent with a reflective gaze.
Soft, funny patterned body.
Prickly, goose-pimpled tongue.
His tail, long and supple.
Smoothly oozing power as he leaps.
His voice is long, melodious, echoing
Throughout the jungle.
Softly yet swiftly he sneaks away.

Joanna Bolton (10)
Angel Primary School

I Wish I Had . . .

I wish I had a nan,
so I could talk all day long.
I wish I had a little sister
so I could play.

I wish I had a beautiful bike,
so I could ride up to the blue sky.
I wish I had a long limo,
so I could go anywhere exciting
                          in the world.

But most of all I wish,
I had my attractive, charming,
lovely, warm dad with me.

Jubby Ayub (11)
Angel Primary School

Don't Judge A Book By Its Cover

Don't judge people by their size
Or the colour of their eyes.
Don't tease people about their skin,
Put all your insults in the bin.
Make people happy, don't make them cry.
Don't insult them or their heart will die.
Criticising is so cruel,
Don't be mean, just play by the rules.
It's rude to call someone skinny or say that they have blubber.
So in future please don't judge a book by its cover.

Rosanna Horton (9)
Campsbourne Junior School

I WOULD LIKE TO BE . . .

I would like to be a red comma in a picture by Matisse.
I am small and red and long sitting in the middle
of a white rectangle.
A pink squiggly hole punched in the bottom left:
Would it be worthwhile to bounce up to that blue
seaweed shape and make myself a good position,
to get a little extra attention?
No, I'd rather not.
What if another hole got punched when I was moving?
Anyway, the seaweed is rough and it's more
comfortable here.
I am not a perfect comma, nobody would put me in a
piece of writing and I'm proud of that.
A comma's never been put in a painting before,
People will stare forever and wonder what the
painting says.

Christopher Isaaks (10)
Campsbourne Junior School

MATISSE MAGPIE

I would like to be a magpie in a picture by Matisse,
I will be still, I will be silent,
Hovering over the white and blue plain.
I wonder whether I should glide across to the tree
but I don't, I feel this is a sacred place and I
hover in peace.

Julius Dwamena (9)
Campsbourne Junior School

When I'm Being Followed

When I'm being followed,
I feel a squeeze inside of me.

When I'm being followed,
I hold my mum's hand harder.

When I'm being followed,
It's a danger to turn around.

When I'm being followed,
I think of home to bring it closer.

When I'm being followed,
I try to keep on walking.

When I'm being followed,
My spine cracks in half.

When I'm being followed,
Should I turn around?

Then I turn around and see,
A statue of the Queen.

Imogen Waller Lassen (9)
Campsbourne Junior School

The Waterfall's Water

The water is sizzling through the river,
Up and round all day,
Spittin' and splattering in the air,
Through the waterfalls leaping and spinning.
It will all freeze some day,
Now it's all ice.

Katie Leigh-Ellis (9)
Campsbourne Junior School

THE MAGIC BOX

I will put in the box

a plate from a golden stegosaurus paddling in a river
a lizard's claw pierced into a stone
a gargoyle carved into a church.

I will put in the box

a frantic tiger charging at a herd
a fearful reservoir swarming with sharks
a terrified parrot squirming with fear.

I will put in the box

a giant stone thundering at Earth
a massive ocean puncturing the land
a pack of wolves fearing the life out of everything.

I will put in the box

long rapids chasing the crocs
my home riding the jungles
a rainbow made of raindrops.

My box is fashioned from gold and silver,
a ruby on every side and dark blue streaming inside.
I will fly in the box over the high mountains reaching
the clouds.

Hugh Hamilton (8)
Campsbourne Junior School

THE NEW GIRL

He was on his way home when he saw
The new girl.
Arrived at school that day,
The new girl.
Something in the air made him
Follow her.
As the fairies danced around him
He felt a shiver go down his spine.
The new girl turned a corner,
Through an invisible mirror where
Nobody went.
She stepped softly over the river.
The boy followed,
But in the middle of the river he
Began to sink.
His face expressionless.
The boy, looking at the new girl.
The new girl.
The new girl.
Looking at the new girl.

Martha Cooper Thorne (10)
Campsbourne Junior School

THE HEAD TEACHER

He needs a body like a thick blue piece of ice.
A pair of feet like a raging, roaring cheetah,
A head like a red angered aardvark,
A pair of hands like narrow roots,
A voice like violent vapour,
A personality like a man-eating monster.

Mustafa (10)
Campsbourne Junior School

NOBODY NEEDS PERFECTION

I would like to be a boulder in a picture by Matisse,
Among those cherry coloured dots on the sandy
yellow landscape.
I would be a leaf among night sky blue oddly
shaped splashes.

The black specks are like a bared roof
and outside there would be nothingness and bare plains.
I would think about walking towards a dot among a
group of others
behind the shadow of the carved rock of endless blue.
But I'm fine where I am,
Nobody needs perfection
and definitely not me.

Francesca Davies (8)
Campsbourne Junior School

TIGER

He needs
A roar like the waterfalls in Neptune's caves,
Eyes like blaring, blazing fireballs,
His ears as soft as foreign silks,
His tail like a slashing whip,
His body ripples like a calm sea,
Speed like the charging on a battlefield,
His teeth like blades of daggers flashing every
Time the sun catches them,
Claws like curved swords,
A nose like a black oil tanker,
And legs like slim young trees.

Imogen Townley (9)
Campsbourne Junior School

JULIET AWAKES

My frozen body awakes at last,
and I feel my life come back from the past.
I see him not like I had feared,
until I stepped on to the floor.
My love was there but what was wrong?
And then I knew his life was gone.
I wish I had just one more time with him,
but I knew I had to go too.
I pulled the dagger from his pocket
and reached it to my chest,
and I could see the stains of blood.
It was the end for me and my love,
I closed my eyes and my soul floated away.

Penny Bowers (10)
Campsbourne Junior School

JULIET

Her hair was long and curly
Glowing in the midday sun.
Her eyes were stars
Glittering in the deep blue sky,
Her long light blue dress trailed on the floor.
Was water flowing freely down a river?
Her silver shoes sparkled in the soft sunlight.
But although fair Juliet was rich and had
Everything that was possible to have
She was a mouse trapped in a mousetrap.
Poor Juliet was trapped between her greatest
Love and her beloved family.

Katie-Lee Ieronimou (11)
Campsbourne Junior School

JULIET

Her eyes were sparkling waves tossing on the sea,
She had ginger hair shining in the sun,
Her white silk summer dress flowing along the sandy beach.
The lace sewn on to the bottom of her dress glowing like
hundreds of flowers on a long green meadow.
Her satin shoes stepping gently along the beach,
But she was not as she seemed.
Her flowing tears dripped down her face for she is a
fly trapped in a web.
Should she be faithful to her family or could she marry
the Montague she loves?

Clara Bransky (11)
Campsbourne Junior School

INSTRUMENTS

The flute's sound is like lemon drops.
The guitar's sound is like a lion roaring in
the damp, warm jungle.
The saxophone's sound is as rhythmic as the
waves hitting the rocks.
The piano's sound is strong and bold.
The drums sound is like thunder rolling across the sky.

Natasha Allen (9)
Campsbourne Junior School

DESERT

Out in the outback
Out in the outback
Kangaroos are bouncing
Moon is rising
Crocodiles are snapping
Ostriches are running
as
    fast
        as
           rockets.

William Rich (8)
Campsbourne Junior School

THE FULL MOON

Sometimes when the moon is full
I creep out of bed, go downstairs and out the front door,
I play all night with the bears
That hide away in the day.
Then just as it is getting light I say . . .
Goodnight!

Louise Jones (9)
Coldfall Primary School

ANIMAL POEM

An atom of elephants,
A tumble of pigs,
A pocket full of butterflies,
A cuddle of bears,
A water full of fish,
A wing full of whales,
A handful of pigeons,
A log of sharks,
A stomach of creatures,
A mouthful of flies,
A barrel of cockroaches,
A current of bees,
A ball of leeches,
A football of mosquitoes,
A leaf full of worms,
A jug full of cows.

Nadullah Hanan (10)
Gillespie Primary School

THE NORMAL OF STRANGE

A ripple of hippos
A planet full of stars
A barrel full of holes
A mouthful of cars

An eye full of blindness
An aquarium of birds
An iceberg full of lava
A spoonful of nerds

A more full of less
A sadness full of happiness
A meeting of bananas
A beauty full of ugliness

A life full of deaths
A rock full of grass
A hell full of heavens
A fish who thinks he's class

Justin Whitehouse (11)
Gillespie Primary School

A NORMAL WORLD

A chest full of giraffes,
A playpen full of guns,
A sky full of fish,
A bottle full of stars.

A hotel full of jungle,
A handful of whales,
A war full of peace,
A hello full of goodbyes.

An earful of deafness,
An apple full of sweets,
A French dictionary of Spanish,
A beard full of slugs.

A rock-band full of nuns,
A bully full of friendship,
A Madonna full of ugliness,
A funeral full of happiness.

Ebru Karatufek (10)
Gillespie Primary School

GHOST

With a touch of a frost
and a look in the eye
the deadly ghost haunting people
for them to die.
With a chilling cry
and a ghostly crackle he says,
'I've dug your grave,
now get the hell inside!'

Jabed Uddin (10)
Gillespie Primary School

A WORLD WITH THREE COUNTRIES

A murmur of hurricanes,
A startle of rain,
A jar of pigs,
A miraculous stare.

A vicious pair of eardrums,
A sluggish pair of jaguars,
A herd full of snails,
A guard pair of hamsters.

A diminutive pair of giraffes,
A basketball team of crocs,
A school of perfume smelling sharks,
A swimming pool of words.

A world with three countries,
An ensemble of hands,
A school with three rulers,
A pear eating a bear.

Polly Michell (10)
Gillespie Primary School

THE STRANGE OF NORMAL

A bottle of hippos,
An Earth full of stars,
A wave of surfing termites,
An earful of cars.

A bully full of gentleness,
A sea full of fires,
A meat full of vegetables,
A happy full of criers.

A football team of monks,
A heaven full of hells,
A hell full of heavens,
A library full of bells.

A dictionary full of numbers,
A pen full of leads,
A land full of water,
A foot full of heads.

Matthew Spurr (10)
Gillespie Primary School

THROUGH THE HOUSE AND UP THE STAIRS

Come through our pine green door,
Trek through our jungle-like floor.
Be careful, do not trip over our shoes,
Watch out, something could fall on you!
Creep through the front room door,
Be careful or the baby will roar.
As you pass the kitchen you may see
A hungry monster, that's probably me.
Go up the stairs that always creak,
You might make a hole in the stairs if you leap.
Giant spiders may attack if you wreck their webs,
Look there is one that has dropped on your head.
There is a room that is messy you see,
Sit on the bed and wait for me.

Tiffany Wilson (9)
Grange Park Preparatory School

THE ROSE

The roses are red,
Red as the sun,
As red as the queen of beauty,
But not as beautiful as you.
You are as beautiful as the sun,
As the rose,
You are a beautiful girl,
And more beautiful than the rose.

Filiz Shukru (6)
Grange Park Preparatory School

SCHOOL

School is fun
And full of jokes,
Everybody laughs.
Lots of teachers
Make jokes too,
When we're out of class.

Teachers can be really strict,
Just like Mrs C,
She teaches us choir
And the singing too.

Sometimes I get really bored
Working out a sum,
Sometimes teacher might complain
And tell me not to talk.

Femi Agbaje-Williams (8)
Grange Park Preparatory School

FISH

Smooth swimmer
Food catcher
Good sneaker
Water wallower
Tail wiggler
Scaly creature
Slippery slider
Water jumper
Reed hider
Fisherman got yer!

Lucy Portsmouth (9)
Grange Park Preparatory School

THE MUSIC SEA

The fisherman has come on his metal flute,
With the gentle *'ting'* of the triangle, as each careless
wave drifts the boat along, then -
'Crash!'
Cry the cymbals,
As clouds crowd together, then -
'Boom!'
Shout the drums, as the lightning strives to
the boisterous, raging sea.
Then a ship comes, with the importance of a trumpet,
But lightning arrives and the ship sounds its
horn as it drowns -
Then sinks.

The fisherman has come on his metal flute,
Feeding the starving mermaids his piccolo crabs,
With the harp of dolphins,
Then his day has ended with the sad
mellowing tune of the final violin.

Rebecca Sheppard (9)
Grange Park Preparatory School

MY MILLENNIUM RESOLUTION

To help and respect people.
To forgive people for what they do wrong.
To not fight back when you are in a fight.
To respect the earth.
To make a new start.

Natalie Hayward (9)
Grange Park Preparatory School

CLOUDS

Fluffy clouds in the sky,
above the treetops.
Look closely at the clouds
and they'll be shaped
like different sorts of things.
Some are white, some are grey,
some of them carry rain.
The summer clouds are nice and bright.
The winter clouds are grey.
Some clouds go together,
some clouds are orange, some are pink
and some clouds are yellow.

Annaliza Ranetunge (7)
Grange Park Preparatory School

SNAKE

Slow slitherer
Sly eyed
Crinkly scaled
Slimy feeler
Turning twister
Hissing lisper
Curling coiler
Professional sneaker
Bitter biter
Mighty fighter
Scary frightener!

Caroline Clarke (9)
Grange Park Preparatory School

THE SEA

The sea is like an orchestra,
The waves crash together like big bass drums,
While under the water mermaids swim and make bubbly
                                    sounds like the harp.
The screeching seagull's like a squeaky piccolo,
The French horn like a ship far out at sea.
Lobsters snip their claws like castanets,
The triangle like a small boat cruising on the deep, soft sea.
The wind blows the sand like you blow a clarinet,
The caves under the sea, deep like a cello,
The cymbals clash together like the waves crash against the cliffs.

Charlotte Watkins (9)
Grange Park Preparatory School

CHRISTMAS

C andles brighten up the night as
H appy children say goodnight.
R eindeer pull Santa's sleigh
I   n the snow on a winter's day.
S anta puts in the stockings,
T oys, books and puzzles too.
'M erry Christmas' he shouts and he waves
'A nd a happy new year too.' Then
S anta rides away on his white sleigh.

Nina Smith (10)
Grange Park Preparatory School

THE BED MONSTER

Last night I thought I saw a monster
under the bed.
I tried to forget him,
I read and read.

Although I knew very well
it had to be a dream,
I just couldn't help it
I let out a scream.

My dad came running
and nearly slipped on a stair,
I cuddled up close to him,
Oh don't we make a lovely pair!

Alexandra Zetter (8)
Grange Park Preparatory School

FIREWORKS

F   ireworks explode into the night sky.
I   wish a firework rocket wasn't so loud
R   iding in the air and exploding a lovely pattern,
E   xploding and sparkling like a chandelier
W   hizzing through a black sky and making it day,
O   range, green, blue and red, nobody knows what comes next.
R   ound and round spins the Catherine wheel,
K   indly the fireworks zoom and then *bang!*
S   parkling and flashing in the night sky.

Zuriye Hilmi (10)
Grange Park Preparatory School

THE DRAGON

A ferocious, spiky, fire-breathing dragon
Walking down the town,
Stomping and stamping and
Wriggling up and down.

A gigantic, enormous dragon
Roaring down the street,
Killing, lashing and fighting
Everyone he meets.

The knight so strong
Is now so weak.
He was hurt by the dragon
In a battle last week.

Susan Bush (9)
Grange Park Preparatory School

MY MILLENNIUM RESOLUTION

Let there be peace on Earth,
No more wars,
And no more fights.
Think about other people,
Especially before you put yourself first,
Don't be vain, and don't be mean,
If we work together,
We can make the world a better place.

Sadia Sapsard (10)
Grange Park Preparatory School

HOUSES

Long house,
short house,
great house,
new house,
old house,
all different houses,
some fat,
some small,
all different houses,
mansions, huts,
some houses low,
some houses high,
castles and igloos,
all different houses,
some houses disgusting,
some houses sparkling,
and some just . . .

Eleanor Burgess (10)
Grange Park Preparatory School

SNOW

Snow falls down every year,
I shiver and I quiver.

Snow is light, snow is bright,
It is very cold at night.

When I am outside at night
I shiver and get a fright.

Elianna Panayiotou (7)
Grange Park Preparatory School

THE MOUSE

There's a mouse in my house
And it's crunched all the crisps,
It's eaten all the apples, even the pips.

There's a mouse in my house
And it's nibbled all the cheese,
It's swallowed all the sweetcorn and some of the peas.

There's a mouse in my house
And it's chewed every snack,
I put it outside but it keeps coming back.

Amy-Louise Ball (8)
Grange Park Preparatory School

SPOOKY OLD HOUSE

Down my road is a spooky old house,
Where no one goes in and no one goes out,
No lights switch off yet no lights switch on,
Its windows are small yet its doors are so long.
The rusty old building sends shivers down my spine,
If I had to live there, I know I would die,
I'm sure when it's midnight
Arising from its ditch,
Are ghosts and aliens, maybe even a
            Witch!

Sophie Crouch (9)
Grange Park Preparatory School

A CHINATOWN PARADE

There is a big dragon
coming up the street,
scaly, spiky,
with big, green feet.

Lashing his tail,
looking at me with his
big, black eyes
and twenty feet.

He's red, blue, green and purple
with a very surprising length.
All the people cheer
as he comes near,
'The Chinatown parade dragon is here!'

Katherine Taylor (9)
Grange Park Preparatory School

THE LOFT

Step up the creaky ladder,
up into the loft,
you don't know what you could find,
it could be hard or soft.
Old teddies, clothes or toys,
things you've been looking for,
books, pencils, tins of things,
even kitchen clocks.
Whatever you find in the loft
I hope that it's not smelly socks!

Victoria Carrington (9)
Grange Park Preparatory School

SUNNY DAYS

B   eaches all around me
A   nd lots of clear, blue sea,
H   appy hour six till seven
A   round the pool, I'm in heaven.
M   asks on, snorkelling near the shore,
A   nimals and fish I've never seen before,
S   unbathing in the Bahamas.

E   ngland is cold,
N   ow I'm home,
G   one is the tan,
L   ong are the nights,
A   lways cold,
N   o eating out,
D   reary England.

Caroline Carlson (11)
Grange Park Preparatory School

CLOUDS

Clouds are beautiful, in summers bright.
Clouds are wonderful, in spring's sight.
Clouds are struck on stormy days.
Clouds are beautiful in some ways.

Clouds are white, fluffy balls.
Clouds are white cotton wool.
Clouds are blue, my favourite colour.
Clouds are cool when it rains.

Ayodele Olaofe (7)
Grange Park Preparatory School

SPAIN

I go to Spain every year,
I go with my friends, they live quite near.
We have a pool which is our own,
I'm so busy - no time to moan.

We have a villa on three floors,
Sparkling tiles and lots of doors.
It has a badminton court at the back,
We never have to use our macs.

The children play every day,
We go to the beach and sit on the bay.
Some of us swim in the sea,
But someone is scared and that is me.

Victoria Chase (11)
Grange Park Preparatory School

SNOW

When snow comes every year
It's white, it's bright, it's very clear.
I wrap up very warm.
It starts to storm.
I like the snow, I sometimes quiver,
It comes at Christmas and makes us shiver.
It snows again, it's very white,
It makes the earth nice and bright.

Amber Spinthiras (7)
Grange Park Preparatory School

THE LAST DAY OF TERM

Finally the time has come,
My time with friends is nearly done.
These people I have known since I was small
And now I have to leave them all.

The times we've laughed and sometimes cried,
The times we've been mean and sometimes lied,
But now we must go our separate ways
But we'll never forget our childhood days.

With tears in my eyes, feeling a fool,
I get ready to go to secondary school.
Saying goodbye to teachers and friends,
Now it has all come to an end.

Amy Crouch (11)
Grange Park Preparatory School

THE HIBERNATING MOUSE

Once I saw a mouse
Hibernating in his house.
I woke him accidentally,
I stroked him very gently.

I think he actually liked me,
I went to get my mum to see.
I asked my mum if I could -
And she said 'Yes,
Keep him.'

Lana McCaskill (8)
Grange Park Preparatory School

THE JOURNEY

The coach swallowing up the road,
Other coaches signalling with a code.
The hot sun beaming through,
I'm stuck in here until around two.
I'm dehydrating,
It's so frustrating,
The journey.

Everyone's out to complain,
They're playing a noisy game, they're all going insane.
Italian roads just seem so long,
People at the back singing my worst song.
We're going nowhere,
How long till we're there?
The journey.

Sophie Redburn (10)
Grange Park Preparatory School

THE GIGANTIC DRAGON

When you see the flame,
You will feel the pain.
You won't be able to say your name.

He has spikes on his back,
Its tail will give you a whack.

You will get a big fright
Especially on a dark night.

Libby Smith (8)
Grange Park Preparatory School

EXAM HORRORS

11+ exam's dawning,
Waking up on exam morning,
Heading to the huge, overcrowded school,
Thinking I am the unclever fool.
Loads of children piling in,
Being put into groups from A-Z,
Led down the hall by giant girls,
Seeing all the new looks and smells.
Arriving in the classroom, sitting down,
Start paper, look at new questions I have found.
Break at last, paper ended,
My mind feels like it's been blended
Into science, English and maths,
Writing down all the facts.

Holly Brink (10)
Grange Park Preparatory School

THE DRAGON

There's a dragon in a village
Stomping all around,
Thrashing and mashing
And tearing things down.

A fierce looking dragon
Terrorising the men,
They were so scared they ran
Back again.

Jessica Carlson (8)
Grange Park Preparatory School

SPIDERS

Pitter-patter, coming near,
A hairy spider, my worst fear.
Running around the bathroom, climbing in the bath,
If I watch him closely, I can see him laugh.
'Dad,' I call,
Now I've seen them all.

Each type of spider running all around,
They even run on the ceiling, but mostly on the ground.
Dad comes in with paper and card,
Mum starts screaming, 'Put it in the yard.'
'No, kill it Dad,' that's what I say,
'Then it won't come back another day.'

Philippa Ware (10)
Grange Park Preparatory School

THE SEASONS

Winter is the time that is cold
And when the animals rest.
Autumn is when the leaves go gold,
Gold brown and red.
Spring is a time when the bulbs grow and
Daffodils and tulips show their colours.
Summer is the time when we go on holiday,
Have picnics, ride bikes and go out to play.

Lauren Harvey (8)
Grange Park Preparatory School

GOODBYES

I find goodbyes very hard,
I've had quite a few, all in all.
One dark and frosty morning,
With dew resting on the grass
My brother tumbled into the garden
With fish flakes held tight in his palm.
Then one minute later he called in to me,
'Sarah, come quick, emergency.'
I ran through the garden, shocked at his cry,
Peered into the pond, nothing.
We blame it on the cat next door,
He's known to be a villain.

Sarah Mortimer (10)
Grange Park Preparatory School

THE DYING OF THE DAY

Lying on the grass in the park,
The sky is gradually getting darker,
A great flame of orange flares
As the sun sinks down.
Tongues of pink and purple lap the sky
Until the sun has melted into the horizon,
Then the black cloak of night is unfolded
And the pitch black sky is littered with stars.
Time to go home, home, home,
Before the darkness gets you!

Elizabeth Eisen (10)
Grange Park Preparatory School

ANDREX PUPPIES

Andrex puppies roll about
in the garden too,
investigate round the house
and always eat their food.

They go for walks in the park,
run about all day,
play with their toys
and make lots of noise.

They sleep in a bed,
love being fed
and like to be cuddled.

Laura Jayne Lewis (8)
Grange Park Preparatory School

GRANGE PARK SCHOOL

Grange Park School started seventy-five years ago,
It stands in the middle of the whole street.
Grange Park Prep is very noisy at playtime,
Quiet in learning,
Rowdy at lunch.

Grange Park School is like work,
We always have jobs to do
And we have to come at the exact time.
Grange Park was the olden days for me,
But now I'm going. Goodbye. Goodbye.

Alexia Loizides (10)
Grange Park Preparatory School

PENGUINS

When penguins tilt to one side,
It means they've got an itch,
They can't help doing it
And it looks a good trick.

Penguins can swim with great skill,
They're also furry too,
You can go and visit them
At London Zoo.

Helena Savva (8)
Grange Park Preparatory School

THE SUN

The sun is big, yellow and bright
and without it there would be eternal night.
The sun is glowing high in the sky
and without it, we would all die.
I know you think the sun is just a big, red sphere,
but if I were you I wouldn't get too near.

I know the sun is a yellow star
and in about 2,000,000 years it will expand very far.
The sun is very high in the sky
and now it's time for me to say goodbye,
because the sun has set.

Holly Millard (8)
Grasmere Primary School

An A-Z Of Things That Happen In Spring

Animals are born,
Birds sing in the young corn,
Crocus appear,
Daffodils and tulips pop out of their buds,
Every tree is budding, every bush too. Can you feel it?
Frogs are spawning,
Goats are kidding,
Hens are laying,
Insects are crawling,
Jenny (the cat) has kittens too, there are five altogether,
                                        aren't they sweet?
Kittens are pouncing, puppies are playing,
Lambs are as white as snow and so cute.
Mum is happy too.
Next week will be just as good I'm sure.
On Wednesday I'm going to help deliver some piglets.
Piglets are wonderful.
Quarrelling is only a distant memory.
Riding Blackberry through the valley is my heaven,
Summer will be along soon.
The day is almost at an end,
Under the blossoming apple tree is the chicken shed, all quiet.
Very tired now,
Want to sleep.
Xylophone is kicked across the floor,
Yawn,
Zzzzzzzzzzzzz.

Katy Ings (9)
Grasmere Primary School

THE CRASH

The start was a bull charge
As they all came to the first corner,
It was a tight squeeze, someone had to go off.
Michael Schumacher (it's a long name, so let's
                                    call him MS)
MS, he was going fast.
As Eddie Irvine tried to pass MS, then it went wrong.
'Eddie Irvine made him go off at 150mph
Into the red and white tyre wall!
The race officials ran to the car.
MS can't get out of the car!'
The race officials help him get out,
He broke both his legs.
Boring Mika Hakkinen won again.
Brave MS. He was so close to
Winning the championship.

Michael Alhadeff (9)
Grasmere Primary School

THE RED DRAGON

Hot and fiery,
burning bright,
it comes out
in the middle of the night,
cursing hunters,
cursing light,
this dragon
doesn't want to fright.

Jaime Ackroyd (9)
Grasmere Primary School

THE TUDORS

The Tudors, the Tudors,
Chopping people's heads off,
That's what they did all day,
Well, that's what it seemed like anyway.

Rich and poor people were different,
The rich had money and fancy clothes,
The poor had rags and no money.

The houses were made out of stone,
Brick and straw roofs,
Some people lived in the country
And some people lived in the town,
And that's what I'm telling you now.

Hannah Leddy (8)
Grasmere Primary School

DEATH

Death is something that comes once in a lifetime,
it always comes at the end.
When you meet death, you will never do anything again.
First of all, your heart skips a beat,
you take one last breath,
then you meet and shake hands with the figure of death.

Alanna Downey-Orr (8)
Grasmere Primary School

THE TRAIN

The train is a pain,
It rumbles like a tumble of boulders,
Its engine, as noisy as a drill,
It smells like strong, rotten eggs,
It looks like hell
With lights like fire
And the chairs, like devils.
It's time to get out
From hour and hour of power,
So I'm out of here, back to heaven.

Sam Roberts (8)
Grasmere Primary School

THE FORMULA 1 RACE

I'm writing about a Formula 1 race.
There goes Michael Schumacher in first place,
Then comes Eddie Irvine in second place
Saying to Michael Shumacher 'in your face.'
'Disqualified,' say the stewards to Eddie Irvine in his car,
Then the stewards say to Eddie Irvine, 'You won't go far.'
Yes, there goes Michael Schumacher speeding past the finish line,
Then he says to himself, 'I'm so fine.'

Luke Kidd (9)
Grasmere Primary School

ANIMALS

First there is a frog who lives in the water
And his daughter is as fat as you.
Secondly, there is an elephant who lives on safari,
Bigger than a tree trunk.
Thirdly, there is a cheetah who's as fast
As a racing car in town.
Fourth, there is a fish
Who swims a hundred miles an hour.
Fifth, there's a tiger who is as loud
As the biggest dish falling on the floor.
Sixth, there is me and I'm running for the door.

Ceyda Ahmet (8)
Grasmere Primary School

BULLY POEM

Her legs were as big as trees,
Her heart jumped with glee,
'Cause she's a big, big, bully.
She punches, she slaps and she
Makes you graze your knees,
At least, that's what happened to me.
Help, she's running after me!
She's going to laugh with glee.
Help me!

Becky Draper (9)
Grasmere Primary School

WHY?

There's a football,
Kick,
Now it is in my face.
Why?

There's an axe,
Swing,
I seem to have lost some of my finger.
Why?

There's a lion,
Growl!
It is scratching me.
Why?

There's a plug and water.
Buzzap!
I am shocked.
Why?

There's a time bomb.
A time bomb?
3 . . . 2 . . . 1 . . .

Rory Norton (8)
Grasmere Primary School

THE ELEPHANT

He had grey skin like the grim king,
his gigantic ears were as big as him,
he must have heard everything,
definitely the king shouting at him.
His trunk was as fat as a tree trunk
and as short as a bicycle pump.
He had an axe for the tigers
That went angry to the max.

Charlie Davis (9)
Grasmere Primary School

GUINEA PIGS

Squeak, squeak, squeak
when you feed them.
Squeak, squeak, squeak
when you take them out.
Squeak, squeak, squeak
when you love them.
Squeak, squeak, squeak
and they love you.

Julia Kinch (9)
Grasmere Primary School

MATTHEW

Matthew is big and tall,
He is even strong.
He has brown shoes that
He wears nearly every day.
Matthew gets into a mess,
Nobody can take it anymore.
He helps everyone too.

Emma Cook (8)
Grasmere Primary School

WAR AND PEACE

War is a time to destroy,
War is a time of demolition,
War is a time for satisfaction,
War is a time to crush with joy,
War is a time with sadness, no joy.

Peace is a time to relax,
Peace is a time to lay back,
Peace is a time to spread your wings,
Peace is a time to do your things,
Peace is a time to jump and sing.

War is a time to kill in destruction,
Peace is a time to live in harmony,
War is a time to always remember,
Peace is a time to celebrate November.

Isha Campbell (11)
Hazelbury Junior School

I Am The Wind

I am the wind that blows the glistening sand,
I am the wind that rustles the autumn leaves,
I am the wind that tangles my shiny, soft hair,
I am the wind that roams the earth,
I am the wind that forces grass off the ground,
I am the wind that cuts past peoples faces,
I am the wind that rushes by,
I am the wind that travels through the sky,
I am the wind that turns my face golden.

Romina Sartori (11)
Hazelbury Junior School

The Sun And Moon

The sun is filled with shining light,
It blazes far and wide.
The moon reflects the sunlight back,
But has no light inside.

I think I'd rather be the sun
That shines so bold and bright,
Than be the moon that only glows
With someone else's light.

Jamila Yusuf (10)
Hazelbury Junior School

Up, Up And Away

Up, up and away in my pink balloon I fly,
When I look up I see the beautiful bright blue sky.

If I look down, birds are flying all around.
Trees, houses and tall buildings look so small now on the ground.
It really is so quiet, you cannot hear a sound.

Some clouds are changing colour now,
Some white, some grey.
Oh no, I spoke too soon, it's now a stormy day!

Jodie Nicholson (9)
Hazelbury Junior School

I Am The Song

I am the song that sings the bird,
I am the leaf that grows the land,
I am the tide that moves the moon,
I am the stream that halts the sand,
I am the cloud that drives the storm,
I am the Earth that lights the sun,
I am the fire that strikes the stone,
I am the day that shapes the hand,
I am the word that speaks the man.

Manal Abdulahi (10)
Hazelbury Junior School

The Four Seasons Of Joy

In spring you can enjoy seeing
wonderful, bright-coloured flowers blooming,
this is a great time when you can start caring
for others and your environment
and you should always help those
that are less fortunate than you.

Summer is a great time when you can
rest and finally have summer holidays.
If you want to, you can even go on holiday.
You can relax in the sun,
you can swim in the crystal blue water,
but you have to remember that life
isn't like this all the time,
so have fun while you can
because if you think life is easy
you will get nowhere.

In autumn, you can step through the
golden brown crispy leaves
and smell the refreshing breeze.
You can see that all of the plants
are dying out and the leaves in the trees
are falling down since it is nearly winter.
Enjoy autumn while you can
because there is nothing like an autumn evening.

Christmas is a part of life
when you can spend great time
with your family, a time when you can play
snowball fights and make snowmen,
A time when you can give or receive gifts.
There are lots of gifts in life,
but the best gift of all is
being with your family at Christmas.

Jacques Malecaut (11)
Hazelbury Junior School

TANKA

We will stay as friends
As long as we shine brightly
And the wind ceases,
I agree with your response
And we will stay friends long.

Our lives are filled with . . .
Happiness and laughter
And our calls and letters
Will make our friendship linger,
Onwards our friendship will grow.

Ramiya Lakshman (11)
Hazelbury Junior School

THE BULLY

Do not be afraid
of Billy the bully.
He is rather silly
and that's Billy.

He has no friends
but he doesn't care,
but inside, there is fear.

Billy the bully is just so silly
and he always picks on Milly
which is quite silly.

Iesha Ryan (11)
Hazelbury Junior School

UNITED

When I look into your eyes
I see that you're just the same as me.
No matter what colour we are,
You're just like me.
When I look into the mirror,
I see I have a face just like you.
No matter what race we are,
African, Asian or even European,
We're all united living under the sun.

Sinem Sipahioglu (10)
Hazelbury Junior School

Up, Up And Away

High up into the sky
I can still see it with my eye,
It looks just like a tiny dot,
I hope it doesn't drop.
It's such a beautiful day,
Go on balloon, up, up and away.

Andrea Davis (9)
Hazelbury Junior School

I Am The Wind

I am the wind that blows the leaves,
I am the wind that rules the Earth,
I am the wind that tangles your hair,
I am the wind that makes the storms,
I am the wind that blows the glittery sand.

Kareena Duck (10)
Hazelbury Junior School

Balloons

The balloons are big and fat and round,
I hold them tightly in my hand.
Red, orange, blue and gold,
As I let go, they gently float
Up, up and away into the sky.

Jade Marshall (8)
Hazelbury Junior School

POEM ABOUT SEA LIFE

Colourful fish and entertaining dolphins,
How beautifully you swim through the deep blue sea.
So fluent are your actions as you get up to all sorts of tricks.
You dip and dive, deep, deep down under,
In and out of the sharp rocks, yet you never seem to hurt yourself.

Do you hear what humans say?
'You're only a mammal with a fishy sense of humour
From the deep, blue sea.'
Yet you always look so happy
With a big smile across your face.

I wonder what you think of us humans who stand and stare
At your clever, quick, sharp, lively movements.
They try to trick you into their terrible nets, to catch you
For their dinner.

We never see you cry, but then the salt water will clean your eyes
And wash away your tears.
We hear you sing sad songs for the friends you lost,
They were trapped in frightful terror in the fisherman's net
Where they had their last sleep.

To all those humans who kill our sea life
How evil, how cruel to kill like this.
Would you like it if it were you?
Make our sea a better, safer place,
Stop killing and think for once.
Don't you love to hear the dolphins sing?
I think it's magnificent.
I'll tell you something, I *don't* want you to do,
Make dolphins extinct.

Andrew Sotiriou (11)
Hazelbury Junior School

UP, UP AND AWAY

Up, up and away
I heard them all say.
I looked up at the sky,
I wonder if it will fly?
It was oval and very large,
Nearly as big as a barge.
Oh this is going to be a hard task,
What is it? You may ask.
Hot air will make this rise,
Now have you guessed the surprise?
Yes, it's an airship, I say,
There she goes, up, up and away.

Jade Ruggieri (11)
Hazelbury Junior School

UP, UP AND AWAY

Up, up and away in my furry balloon
With my champagne and caviar, I'll be home soon!
Over Paris, Milan and stop-off at New York,
Then back down the Atlantic and over to Cork.
Take a dip in the ocean and race with a plane,
Then landing in China for chicken chow mein.
A detour in Australia, a stop-off in France,
Then over to India for a traditional dance.
Down to Africa where the wild cats play,
Then home to Edmonton,
No more up, up and away!

Pietro Catalano (9)
Hazelbury Junior School

I LIKE!

I like computers because they are intelligent,
I like skipping ropes because they are fun,
I like burgers because they are tasty,
I like a lot of things, what about you?
I like books because they are great,
I like TV because it is interesting,
I like jokes because they are funny,
I like a lot of things, what about you?

Meisha Watson (9)
Hazelbury Junior School

SPIRIT WORLD

Sleep . . . down . . . floor . . . ground . . .
The boy felt like he was floating, drifting,
Flying through the smoky, misty, dry, grey air.
His brain couldn't work anymore,
His body was crawling on the floor.
All he could hear was *wooh . . . wooh.*
Then he heard two creepy voices saying,
'We're coming, we're coming . . .'

He tried to get up and run,
But the ghosts were everywhere around him
Wherever he looked.
'You're going to stay here
Forever . . . forever . . . *forever!*'
He screamed as loud as a hawk,
'*Noooooooooo!*'

'What's the matter dear?' said his mum.
'Thank goodness' he thought,
'I'm safe at last.'
He opened his eyes and looked at his mum.
She had a *big* devil monster face.
He screamed '*Aaaahhhh! Nooooooo!*
Noooooooo!
His mum took off the mask and said,
'Happy Hallowe'en!'

Tashan Evans (8)
Hungerford School

The Staffroom

The staffroom door was always closed
No one ever saw anyone go in,
and no one ever saw anyone come out.

Until one day some little soul decided
he had had enough.

So one cold morning he declared
he was going in.

He crept up the stairs and stood on the landing
hoping no one was there.

So he pulled the handle down as quietly as a mouse
and pushed the door open.
Then suddenly he saw . . .
Teachers drinking tea.

Katie Phillips (11)
Martin Junior School

Colours

What is red? Red is an apple that is juicy.
What is yellow? Yellow is a sun that shines every day.
What is pink? Pink is a rose that is beautiful.
What is green? Green is grass which is a plant.
What is purple? Purple is a flower that is pretty.
What is blue? Blue is the sky that has clouds.

Chisato Isozaki (10)
Martin Junior School

FIREWORKS

F   is for a furious family of fireworks flashing in the sky,
I   is for an incredible introduction to the impressive fireworks,
R   is for the rough remains of the rocketing fireworks,
E   is for the most entertaining embroidery of the swirling fireworks,
W   is for wonderful, whistling, whirling fireworks,
O   is for the original, occasional fireworks dancing in the sky,
R   is for the royalty of the rocketing, re-emerging fireworks,
K   is for the keen, keeping, kicking fireworks in the sky,
S   is for the sizzling, scorching, steaming, swift, solemn, swirling and
    swishing fireworks in the sky!

Faizah Ahmad (11)
Martin Junior School

THE PIRATE GHOST

They called him the pirate ghost. He was a very mean pirate who was
the captain of a very mean crew. They killed him because he was so evil
he killed people for nothing.

A long, long time ago in Denmark there lived a man who was a pirate.
He liked to think that he and his crew could get the magic map that
would lead to the treasure that no one had ever got.

So that day they went away. From that day people never saw them
again. People say they see ghosts that look like him, strange but true.

Daniel Balogun (10)
Martin Junior School

THE CHOCOLATE CAKE

Chocolate cake I saw on the table,
I wanted to eat it, and I knew I was able,
but I'd save it till school,
if I ate it there, I might look cool.

I was on my way to the playground,
Oh no, the cake might have turned into a horrible mound,
I opened the golden paper,
Ooh! I wished I was a chocolate maker.

I saw the brown delicious food,
I knew I was in exactly the mood,
to gulp it right down,
right into my throat.

I was just about ready to take a big bite,
I could eat this all day until night,
So I went and took a big bite,
'*Aaah!* Delicious.'

Edwin Fairbrother (11)
Martin Junior School

YELLOW

Y   olk is runny and sticky,
E   veryone likes yellow clouds,
L   ook at the chicken's egg,
L   emons are my favourite food.
O   h! Those are nice melons.
W ow! Look at the colours in the sky, it is bright.

Louise Hudson (11)
Martin Junior School

THE GHOST

G hosts are scary
   but they're not real.

H aunted houses are not true
   but people just say they're real.

O ranges are sour and some people love them and some hate them
   I don't think ghosts like them.

S pooky houses and spooky ghosts
   they're not really true.

T he scary ghosts think they're scary
   but they are not.

Maria Pereira (10)
Martin Junior School

SAMMY THE SURFING SEAL

Sammy the surfing seal, he slides, he slithers
on the sea.
He surfs on his surfboard up the high waves
and always lands in the darkest caves.

Of course he sounds cool, but he's still very dim
Sammy's still learning how to swim.

Sammy the seal loves surfing
He loves it!
He loves it!
He loves surfing!

Jason Hancock (11)
Martin Junior School

THE DARK SHADOW

It was a really dark night when I saw a shadow at my window.
It was saying 'Sunny, sunny, sunny . . .'
I was so scared that I ran under my bed,
And I started to cry.

I looked again at the window and the shadow was gone.
I was scared, and because of that, I went to my mum's bedroom,
but she was not there.
So I started to cry some more, then I listened again, 'Sunny, sunny . . .'
So I went to my room and went to my bed.

The shadow was tall, fat and black.

'Sunny, sunny, sunny . . .'

Tania Abrantes (10) & Livia Nascimento (11)
Martin Junior School

UP, UP AND AWAY

To north,
To heaven,
around and about,
across the ocean,
for my potion,
back home again to my lotion
can't sit down,
must fly again.
To north,
to heaven,
around and about,
past my home,
without a doubt.

Sophie Gowland (10)
Martin Junior School

COUNTING

One and one are two,
Tie the laces on your shoe,
Two and two are four,
Stop knocking on my door,
Three and three are six,
Come on! Let's do some tricks,
Four and four are eight,
Oh, shoot! Someone broke our gate,
Five and five are ten,
Look I bought a new pen.
Now that you know what to do,
you can do it again tonight,
even when you're in the loo,
keep on doing it until you get it right.
One, two, three and four,
don't stop there, count more,
Five, six, seven, eight,
Hurry up! Or you'll be late,
Nine,
Go on! You're doing fine,
Ten is the last one,
just learn that, and you'll be having fun.

Shahara Begum (11)
Martin Junior School

FIRST STEPS

Oops-a-daisy, tumble and rise
come on sugar plum, do it for Mum-Mum
left foot, right foot, over again,
Come on, yes, that's it. *Bang!* Oopsy!

Look! There's a swing, do you want to have a go?
Well walk to it, love. C'mon it's about time and you know
all the other kids can do it see,
come on sweetie, walk with me.

Oops-a-daisy, tumble and rise
you didn't expect that sweetness, it was quite a surprise
Oh yes, that's it, honey, you're doing it,
if you start walking you will be really fit.
Wooh, bang! Oopsy!

Well you'll have to walk one day, blossom
you're capable, love, you're just a lazy possum
Dadda can do it and Mama too
everyone can do it except for you.

Oops-a-daisy, tumble and rise
yes, they're your feet so move them . . . Hey!
You're doing it, darling, today's the day
Yoohoo! You've done it, hip, hip, hooray!

Rebecca Robson (11)
Martin Junior School

To North, To South

Around and about,
Past the ocean, to see
Which potion.

High above the clouds,
Into the darkness
Now it's time to go back down
Without any sound.

Here I am at home again,
With no paper or pen
Back in bed,
Nothing more
To be said.

Amy Snell (11)
Martin Junior School

Menu Poem

First course - potatoes and beans is a good start for the first meal.
Three pounds for the main course, that's a good deal.
Main course - for the main course there is turkey and gravy,
only meat and chicken, no savoury.
Pudding - for pudding there is chocolate cake and ice-cream.
If you bite it at once, it will make you scream.
For the finishing touch there is a cold drink
If you drink it all up, the waiter will give you a wink.

Mary Otumahana (10)
Martin Junior School

Up, Up And Away

I was flying up high,
Then I flew up into the sky,
My wings were flat,
Flat as a black jack.
My wings could make me glide,
Then I landed on a slide.
I then stop,
Then I go pop,
My wings were busted,
They couldn't be trusted,
Then I was dead,
I lay down my head,
That was the end of my life.

Terry Chu (11)
Martin Junior School

My Dinosaur

My dinosaur can roar,
he stretches his legs,
he stamps his feet,
he has sharp paws,
he runs very fast.
He can reach the tree,
he is the hardest dinosaur in the world,
he can eat meat,
he can eat a triceratops and
he can eat a stegosaurus and
he has a long neck.

Mark Earl (10)
Martin Junior School

MY OWN VERSION OF PAINTBOX MUSIC

If I could write black music
It would be cold and spooky music
It would be dark and gloomy music
It would be midnight music.

If I could write yellow music
It would be jolly and happy music
It would be cheerful and playful music
It would be sunny music.

If I could write orange music
It would be hot and flaming music
It would be bright and flashy music
It would be flaming music.

If I could write rainbow music
It would be black and yellow music. It would be orange music.

It would be lovely music.

Emma Louise Crossman (10)
Martin Junior School

MY RABBIT

My rabbit walks carefully and has black and white fur
and has sharp black eyes like an eagle.
When she sees fresh vegetables she suddenly
jumps with joy and catches them.
She eats the vegetables carefully until she finishes the vegetables.
Once upon a time she saw a little bird;
she walked carefully towards the bird.
She felt that it was the right time to jump with all her power
Crash she had got him.

Mostafa Gheedan (9)
Martin Junior School

PAINTBOX MUSIC

If I could write yellow music,
It would be happy and cheerful music,
It would be joyful and jolly music,
It would be a sunny day's music.

If I could write white music,
It would be plain and boring music,
It would be dull and cloudy music,
It would be snow music.

If I could write gold music,
It would be bright and sparkling music,
It would be surprising and shiny music,
It would be the stars' music.

If I could write orange music,
It would be bright and exciting music,
It would be cheerful and jolly music,
It would be an orange's music.

If I could write multi-coloured music,
It would be yellow and white music,
It would be gold and orange music,
It would be the world's music.

Cigdem Tanrioglu (10)
Martin Junior School

THE MAGIC BOX

I will put in my box

The glow of a candle in the midnight sky,
a drop of dew on a flower,
and a flap of a sparrow's wing.

I will put in my box

The colour running from a pencil
the first thought of a child
and the sand trickling through fingers.

I will put in my box

The dusty smell of a favourite bear
the lick of a dog against warm fingers,
and the pride of a lion.

My box is fashioned out of moonglow and stardust
with whispers on the lid and laughter in the corner
The hinges are tickles of a tiny baby.

I shall give my box
to the poor girl on the street
and as she smiles
I shall be happy.

Miriam Starling (10)
Martin Junior School

STORMY NIGHT

As the stormy night came by
Everyone knew they were going to die.

The clutter and clatter of the storm
made everyone swarm like bees.

The lights went out
We heard everyone shout *'Help!'*

It smashed houses off
away and across.

Then it got quiet
really quiet.

And it never crashed there
Again.

No one survived!

Redmond Hinds (10)
Martin Junior School

THE RAIN

The rain is *pouring* down my face.
The rain is *crashing* on my feet.
The rain is *splashing* on the road.
The rain is *sparkling* in my hair.
The rain is *rolling* off my car.
The rain is *gushing* to the street.
The rain is *dropping* off the bin.
The rain is *rumbling* on my roof.

Demi Wan (9)
Martin Junior School

STORMY NIGHT

It was a stormy night
Doors creaked
Gates slammed
Fierce winds blew down trees.

Dogs howled
Children cried
People shivered in fright.

Trees shuffled,
Birds fluttered
Cars were overturned.

Finally winds went silent
Gates stopped slamming
The storm had left the night.

Vincenzo Di-Trolio (9)
Martin Junior School

THE RAIN

The rain is *gushing* down the street.
The rain is *falling* on my feet.
The rain is *leaking* while I'm peeking.
The rain is *going* down the drain while I'm in pain.
The rain is *slashing* while the light is flashing.
The rain is *rushing* and I'm blushing.
The rain is *floating* and I'm going boating.
The rain is *drifting* and I'm lifting.
The rain is *stopping* now I am *popping*.

Jazmin O'Driscoll (8)
Martin Junior School

THE STORMY NIGHT

I couldn't sleep because there was a strong breeze,
There was a rustling in the old, old trees.
So I came downstairs and I could hear my clock
And I could hear a loud *tick-tock, tick-tock.*

As I noticed there was nothing wrong
I noticed a bird singing a helpless song
He went *tweet, tweet, tweet.*
Oh how those birds are ever so sweet,
But then the breeze was getting bad
It was going *ooowww,* but it somehow made me sad.
So I ran up the stairs with a *bang, bang, bang*
And went into my mum's room,
The windows were going *cling clang, cling clang.*
So I shut the window and woke up my mum,
She said 'Don't worry, help will come.'

I went down to the basement with my pet dog
And it started to go *woof, woof,* it had caught a hedgehog.
Then the window smashed, there was a barking
And a terrible sound of crashing.

Joe Paine (10)
Martin Junior School

BLUE

B   lue is the colour of the sky in the daytime.
L   ook at the swimming pool and go for a swim.
U   nder the sea there are moving waves.
E   verton has blue football shirts.

Ben Thurgood (10) & Angel Campoveroe
Martin Junior School

PAINTBOX MUSIC

If I could write orange music
It would be a fiery music
It would be hot music
It would be warm music.

If I could write white music
It would be cold music
It would be icy music
It would be sparkling music.

If I could write black music
It would be dark music
It would be dull music
It would be night music.

If I could write gold music
It would be glistening music
It would be bright music
It would be shining music.

If I could write pink music
It would be gentle music
It would be spring music
It would be blossoming music.

If I could write rainbow music
It would be yellow and orange music
It would be red, green and violet music
It would be colourful music.

Winifred Amissah (10)
Martin Junior School

A STORMY NIGHT

The old inn door creaks as the wind blows
Unknown footsteps thud on the old floorboards
Bats screech as fierce rain batters their wings
A white figure walks the gloomy streets.

As people sleep in their beds, quiet, dreamy
Lightning lights the sky and rustles the trees
Still the white figure walks on, into the dead of night.
Owls hoot as thunder crackles and the rain ceases to stop.

Wind howls and doors bang
Windowpanes rattle as the inn bell clangs
Still he walks, never stopping
Till dawn makes its greeting.

Still he does not stop, on this stormy night
Nobody knows who, nobody knows why
Walking, walking he goes, into the dead of night
He has no purpose, no gain, just to walk the streets at midnight
                                        in the pouring rain.

Jessamyn Witthaus (10)
Martin Junior School

A STORMY NIGHT

On one stormy night,
In the old barn,
There was a fight,
In came the wind throughout the night.

And again and again it came,
Trees shuffled and leaves rustled,
It was like an annoying game,
And then even cars were overturned.

All that time,
We were scared,
Because of that, we had to stay inside,
Whistling was all we heard.

Cars crashed with a *boom!*
It was like a typhoon,
I have finished this poem today,
Which will be going up on display.

Michelle T Pereira (10)
Martin Junior School

JUST ONE DAY

In one day I can . . .

Nod my head
and
lie on the bed.

Go to the park
and
the weather goes dark

I am tall
and
fall in the pool.

Get a cat
and
sell a hat.

Dance and sing
and
jump like a spring.

Tushar A Gadhia (9)
Martin Junior School

MAGIC BOX

I will put in my box . . .

A tropical island with sandy beaches,
palm trees with juicy peaches,
and silky snakes slithering silently.

I will put in my box . . .

A souvenir from World War One,
and a heavy pyramid that weighs a ton,
tangled tigers that talk in Taiwan.

I will put in my box . . .

A foot of a dog and a tongue of a cat,
a man in a house trying to catch a rat,
and a mandarin monkey making money.

My box is fashioned out of platinum and steel,
with planets on the lid and giggles in the corners,
Hinges, the first step of man.

I will put in my box . . .

Jasmine Anderson (10)
Martin Junior School

MY T-REX

My T-rex can break trees in one second
and win a scaring contest
because it makes a big sound,
big claws, just hard paws.
It creeps to a dinosaur and waits,
it runs fast, like a car.

Marzban Kapadia (9)
Martin Junior School

PAINTBOX MUSIC

If I could write black music,
It would be cold music,
It would be icy music,
It would be dim music.

If I could write purple music,
It would be swift music,
It would be spinning music,
It would be jazzy music.

If I could write silver music,
It would be magic music,
It would be dizzy music,
It would be airy music.

Nathan Alex Asher (9)
Martin Junior School

UP, UP AND AWAY

Balloons in the air go higher than kites do dare.
Over the ocean in the air.
Hot air balloons, can nearly touch the moons.
Balloons, balloons everywhere,
Go higher than we do dare.
They probably see the planes,
They can go really high can't they?
Up, up and away,
Fly, fly, fly away.
Pop!
The balloon goes,
      down, down, down
          and away.

Aimee Louise Rogers (10)
Martin Junior School

FLY

I'm in my helicopter
It's swooping through the cloudy sky
It is my first time
The cuddly clouds keep me up
A bird is flying down beside me
I tell it how lucky you are to be free.

Jessie Kochan (11)
Muswell Hill Junior School

THE GIANT

The giant having his bath, pulls out the plug,
The rain comes pouring down,
The giant's roar is the sound of thunder.
The rain stops, water runs out of his bath,
The thunder stops as suddenly as it started.

Ella Bruce (8)
Muswell Hill Junior School

THE HAMSTER

The hamster
Cuddly,
Fluffy,
Crawling around my bedroom,
The charming hamster.

Aimee Mackenzie (8)
Muswell Hill Junior School

MILLENNIUM

On the millennium eve
everybody is getting ready
for the late parties to come,
along with the happiness of a new year.
Later people get ready to go
and begin their millennium celebrations.
When the fireworks go off
all the people go 'Ooh' and 'Aah'
when they see the fantastic colours
all shooting into the sky,
like sparks of the rainbow.
Then the countdown starts
'5, 4, 3, 2, 1,
Happy new millennium!'

Mirella Louise Wilson (8)
Muswell Hill Junior School

FLY

Fat pigs can fly,
high in the blue sky.
They sweetly glide through the air,
like an aeroplane with the wings of a bird.
When they get tired they rest on a cloud.
They no longer remember their troubles,
for they are in pig heaven.
They whiz, they shoot like shooting stars,
they fly for ages right on to Mars.
They glide, they swoop, they swoop through the air,
The delightful sensation is too good to share.

Harry Wilson (10)
Muswell Hill Junior School

THE MOUNTAIN

The mountain is very tall
I'm telling you I'd hate to fall,
The summer wind
Blowing my hair
Go on, go on, please go there.

In the winter the icy snow,
Falling softly on my nose.
The snowflakes falling gently down,
It feels like it's pressing me
Hard to the ground.

In summertime
I climb so high,
Reaching up to touch the sky.

Clara Baldock (9)
Muswell Hill Junior School

FLY

Where pigs have wings and chocolate flies
Birds are skies
Their wings are clouds
And there are chocolate pounds
There's chocolate freedom
Chocolate flies
There are toffee pies, I want to fly
Chocolate shoes walk down the street
Every pair I want to eat!

Amalia Randolph (10)
Muswell Hill Junior School

MY MAGIC BOX

Each night when the lights go out
I've brushed my teeth and there is no one about
I climb into my magic box of dreams and wishes
I sit on my swan's back
His wings he swishes
And we fly up high with the birds and the bees
We stop at a party for a cup of tea
Again I crouch on my swan
And the lid I see
I open my eyes to yet another day
I prop up my pillow and shout 'Hip hooray!'

Georgina Stevens (11)
Muswell Hill Junior School

FLY

When I was little
I believed I could fly.
I jumped off the couch
And thought of the sky.
It never worked
Which is plain to see
Because now I understand
The world and gravity.
Although it would be good
To fly like a bird
But people can't fly,
So I have heard.

Emily Haynes (11)
Muswell Hill Junior School

GOD AND HIS ANTI-SPRAY

God was the man who made the world.
The plants and dinosaurs unfurled
But the dinosaurs started quarrelling . . .
So he got out his anti-dino spray
He sprayed them so they went away.

Then he made people come
But the fights and wars were not much fun
Their brains were supposed to be bigger . . .
So what if he gets out his anti-people spray?
Maybe we deserve to die anyway.

Matthew Fallon (8)
Muswell Hill Junior School

MY HAND

I can write with my small hand
I can clap with my round palm
I can catch with my hands.
I can use my finger to spread my lip balm.
I can hold a book with my hand
I have got patterns on my hands
I love my hands
If I did not have any hands
I would not be able to do all these things.

Rasheeda Gafur (10)
Muswell Hill Junior School

CONCORDE

I'd like to be Concorde,
Whizzing through the sky,
Faster and faster I go,
Clouds go zooming by.
I'd like to be Concorde,
The world underneath so small,
Higher and higher I go,
To the world I look so tall.
I'd like to be Concorde,
The sun is not that far,
To all the birds and people,
I look like a shooting star.
I'd like to be Concorde,
The other planes far behind,
I'm the fastest of them all,
But the other planes don't mind.

Hannah Baldock (11)
Muswell Hill Junior School

FLY

At last I'm free from being grounded,
And from my baby brother crying.
I play about with a football
Which makes me feel at home.
A day on the park on the swings
Makes me feel free.
Free as a bird flying in the sky,
And free like a kite in the sky.

Candice Desmuruis (10)
Muswell Hill Junior School

ME

In the morning I wake up very clumsily and slowly.
I put my clothes on dementedly.
I fall down the stairs clumsily.
I play the PlayStation enthusiastically.
I munch my cereal fantastically.
I run to school quickly.
I sit on the carpet crazily.
I do my work chaotically.
I go to break noisily.
I play brilliantly.
I drive home dangerously.

I fling myself on the sofa and
            watch TV gormlesssly.
I scoff my dinner carefully.
I take off my socks bravely.
I go to bed late and beautifully.

Louis Marsh (10)
Muswell Hill Junior School

FOOTBALL

Football is a hard, tough game.
A strict game, but also a fun game.
But then if we want to make it more fun
We should cure all this racist stuff.
Because it is mean and not very nice.
And we should respect and not neglect
All this talent black people have
And not just white.

Caspar Sonnet (11)
Muswell Hill Junior School

THE BOX OF NIGHTMARES

Deep down under the ground,
There lies a black box with gold edges,
And a thick padlock on the front,
A box filled with all the world's
Very worst nightmares.
It lies still and silent,
Filled with war, poverty and disaster,
And murder, death and monsters.
No goodness in this box.
No hope, happiness or fun.
Though it's been opened before,
It now lies guarded by
Thick, dark earth,
And even if all the badness
Is forever fighting to escape,
The box will lie shut
Until the end of time.

Bella Travers (10)
Muswell Hill Junior School

I'D LIKE TO BE A FLOWER

I'd like to be a flower,
to bloom all year round,
and when it comes to night-time
I'd die down to the ground.
I'd wake up in the morning
to see the hot sun rise,
and in the breezy evening
I'd watch the fireflies!

Madeleine Wickers (8)
Muswell Hill Junior School

THE SERPENT

Green, slimy, a myth
Around in Aztec time,
Believed in
Double-headed,
Fierce teeth
Angry eyes.
The serpent.

Joe Bourne (8)
Muswell Hill Junior School

TIME

Time ticking-tocking on the wall.
Making me feel like a ball.
Time flies when you're having fun.
But goes quite slow when you're on the run.
So time is fun, just to run, run, run!

Tillie Holt (9)
Muswell Hill Junior School

THE FIRE

Flames of orange lashing out
the fire's leaping high.
The flames fight until they die
they flash all over.
When the flame dies all is dark.

Louis Schamroth-Green (8)
Muswell Hill Junior School

ME

In the morning I wake up slowly.
Then I run downstairs to watch TV clumsily.
I eat my breakfast noisily.
I get dressed carelessly.
I go to school regularly.
I line up usually.
I sit on the carpet quietly.
I do my homework casually.
I go outside excitedly.
I do my maths confidently.
I read my book carefully.
I eat my lunch messily.
I do my handwriting neatly.
I listen to a story avidly.
I go home finally.
I watch TV happily.
I go to bed sleepily.

Rachel Stanigar (9)
Muswell Hill Junior School

KNICK-KNACKS

I have a load of knick-knacks
they cover every table and floor.
Whenever I buy knick-knacks
I just want more and more.
They're just like chocolate, an obsession.
I love them in my possession
I see them every day
they never go astray.

Eve Katherine Houghton (11)
Muswell Hill Junior School

MILLENNIUM

M illennium celebrations, it's going to be a blast
I n the pub it's gonna' last
L ittle babies don't know what all the fuss is for
L ots of toddlers sitting on the floor
E lephants trumpeting so very loud
N obody can hear them because of the crowd
N ever again shall I eat any cake
I shall bake my own cake
U npleasant party poppers popping in my ears
M illennium party is about to end.

Alexia Argyrou (9)
Muswell Hill Junior School

I LOVE BOOKS

I love books, not because of their looks,
It is just that I could spend hour and hours
with my reading super powers.
Just reading books, books and books.
My reading powers can bite the words I read
as I enjoy reading and picture stuff in my head.
Did you know I can read in the dark in bed?
But I just love books, books.
Not because of their looks.
I just love *books!*

Kristina Goggin (10)
Muswell Hill Junior School

THE FAIRIES

A feather floats down onto a rough branch
Fairies scurry to get onto the small velvet feelers,
Mothers cradle their miniature children in golden acorn shells.
They climb aboard, the feather goes down, down, down
It touches the ground, the fairies jump off,
They run hurriedly to the frozen lake where they dance and sing.
The fairies dance marvellously and have a huge feast of
                                        berries and nuts.
When the children and babies start to whine and doze,
Their parents run quick as the wind and lay them down
Wrapping them in smooth blankets in dry grass.
All the children become quiet and fall into a deep sleep.
The parents dash back to the lake to dance, eat and sing.
The clock strikes 12, they scurry back to their houses in the wise trees,
Gathering their children and clambering onto the uncomfortable rope,
Gathering blankets and going to bed.
And then the same thing happens all over again, repeating itself.

Lois Bond (9)
Muswell Hill Junior School

HORSE RIDING

I love horse riding,
Zooming over the jumps,
Flying like the wind,
Taking a sharp corner,
Then flying again.
Trotting smartly over poles,
Flying fantastically over a hedge,
Glimmering brightly like the sun,
I love horse riding.

Elizabeth Donker-Curtius (9)
Muswell Hill Junior School

THE SOUNDS OF SILENCE

Sometimes at night when I'm lying in my bed,
I listen and I hear the sounds of silence.
First I hear the wonderful call of the owl,
Ringing out into the darkness,
Telling me that night has begun.
Then the soft whispering of the cold wind,
Flying in through the gaps around my window,
Making me shiver under my light, summer blanket.
I listen to the tap-tap-tapping of a branch,
Banging against my window,
Rapping on the panes,
Droning on and on.
Sending me slowly into a peaceful sleep,
A calm and tranquil sleep,
And I dream of the world outside,
Of the owl calling,
And the wind whispering,
And the tree tap-tapping on my window.
I dream wonderful dreams of all these sounds,
The sounds of silence.

Jess Thompson (11)
Muswell Hill Junior School

THE HAUNTED HOUSE

In the haunted house
There's a ghost about,
Whoever goes in, will never come out.
Inside lies a doll without a head,
And a dead man without a leg,
Cobwebs all over the place,
And on the floor lies a battered suitcase,
Next to it is an overgrown vine,
Also on the floor are two or three cases of wine
That really look quite divine.
The ghost is said to be very sly,
With a very slight glint in his eye.
He sits down in the corner of the room
Waiting for someone else to meet their doom!

Joe Beveridge (10)
Muswell Hill Junior School

THE HAUNTED

The haunted house is here to stay
It is painted a really dull grey.
Screams are not heard by day.
In the moonlight the ghosts do stray.
They dodge through the cobwebs easy as prey.
They swing on the chandeliers as it sways.
They have celebrations all in May.
It makes them happy and gay.
Remember the haunted house is here to stay.

David Omoregie (11)
Muswell Hill Junior School

GREEK GODDESSES

Hera is the goddess of marriage and love,
Women look up to her to heaven above,
She's dainty and pretty, best of them all,
Got any problems? Just give her a call.

Aphrodite is goddess of beauty,
Loving and prettiness is her duty,
She's got long blonde hair that goes down to her ankle,
She's got real gold earrings that tinkle and dangle.

If I could choose a goddess to be,
I'd choose the goddess of you and me,
We'd skip around laughing away,
Wasting all of our precious day.

Phoebe Fullbrook (10)
Muswell Hill Junior School

OCTOBER

In October leaves fall down,
when you step on them they crunch.
When it turns to autumn it gets colder.
Conkers fall down on the ground,
people pick them up and leaves turn
red, yellow and brown.
Days are shorter.
You see lots and lots
of spider webs.
In October it is cold.

Isabelle Aron (9)
Muswell Hill Junior School

ME

I wake up clumsily.
I dress carelessly.
I walk down the stairs blankly.
I watch the TV dreamily
I eat my breakfast noisily.
I work carelessly.
I play beautifully.
I come home confidently.
I play my N64 brilliantly.
I slump in front of the TV avidly.
I go to bed chaotically.

Michael Simpson (9)
Muswell Hill Junior School

ME

In the morning I wake up grumpily.
I get dressed blindly.
I go downstairs clumsily.
I eat rapidly.
I watch TV blankly.
I go in the car stupidly.
I go to school casually.
I do my work mentally.
I play madly.
I eat dinner joyfully.
I play on my Nintendo impatiently.

Joe Grant (10)
Muswell Hill Junior School

ME

I wake up slowly.
I munch my breakfast slurpily.
I watch TV sleepily.
I get dressed quickly.
I get to school noisily.
I line up casually.
I sit on the carpet quietly.
I do handwriting carefully.
I play at playtime crazily.
I line up childishly.
I do my work enthusiastically.
I eat my lunch clumsily.
I line up stupidly.
I do literacy smartly.
I play at playtime weirdly.
I do maths sensibly.
I go home happily.
I watch TV blankly.
I scoff my dinner calmly.
I go to bed sadly.

Alexa Lawrence (10)
Muswell Hill Junior School

THE SEA

The sea is a rolling cat
Its paws are the rivers
Whirlpools are its gaping mouth
Islands are the fur
The roaring waves make the sound of purring
Watch out, here's the dog!

Ben Lopez (9)
Muswell Hill Junior School

ME

In the morning I wake up sluggishly.
I get dressed speedily.
I zoom downstairs chaotically.
I slump on the sofa noisily.
I stare at the TV blankly.   '
I chew my breakfast clumsily.
I run to school regularly.
I line up childishly.
I sit on the carpet quietly.
I calculate my maths brilliantly.
I go to play quickly.
I line up sensibly.
I sit on the carpet politely.
I do my work carefully.
I go to the workshop carelessly.
I go home casually.
I watch TV happily.
I go to sleep unhappily.

Avi Walerius (9)
Muswell Hill Junior School

THE SEA

The sea rumbles carelessly
Hitting the rocks wildly.
Evening comes and the sea goes to sleep

Still he's sending pebbles across the shores
Eating the seaweed while he goes by.
A whisper will wake him up, hurry, hurry, before he gets up.

Yoni Pakleppa (8)
Muswell Hill Junior School

TEACHERS

10 teachers relaxing in the staffroom,
9 work books waiting to be filled
8 inspectors inspecting a broom
7 teachers waiting to be bullied
6 students bullying one teacher
5 parents complaining to the Head
4 children not waiting to see their movie feature
3 teachers needing to go to bed
2 teachers already fainted
1 Head shouting at the top of her voice.

Niamh Mealey (9)
Muswell Hill Junior School

THE EAGLE

The eagle gracefully swoops through the sky
turning, swerving and doing loop-the-loops.
His golden feathers fluttering in the warm breeze.
His huge wings glitter as the water reflects
the golden sun.
He spots his prey,
A fish gliding through the water.
He drops straight down and catches
the fish in his talons.

Freddie Duffy (10)
Muswell Hill Junior School

BOX FOR GOOD AND BAD

Good
Wishes and dreams for *children:*
Children's dreams and wishes would be a
toy box full of sweets, toys and comics,
but, on the other hand, *adults* would
wish and dream of winning the lottery,
going on expensive holidays,
being able to retire and relax in front of the TV.
I would wish and dream of becoming rich,
being able to go on expensive holidays,
being really clever so I don't have to go to school.

Bad
A children's worst nightmare:
Their worst nightmare is terrible, it is about
'The Thing' coming to get them.
'The Thing' is a black creature in a black long cloak.
'The Thing' sucks out their souls at night
then takes them to his den.
In the den there are lots of skeletons hanging from the ceiling.
When they are taken to the den, they are never seen again.

Sam Barrett Binney (11)
Muswell Hill Junior School

ALL ON MY OWN

Phone ringing,
TV singing,
Doorbell going,
Nobody knowing,
Open door,
Parcel on floor,
Open up,
Just my luck,
Nothing in,
Just my sin,
Pick phone line
Only dead line,
All on my own,
All alone,
Go to bed,
Feeling dead!

Last night - nightmare gave me a real scare.
Box of dreams killing me,
Felt so real, oh so real!
Silence, silence,
Killing silence!
Feeling like I've fallen out of a plane,
Wind blowing like a pain,
Never, ever, be the same,
Silence, silence, killing silence!

Max Abse (11)
Muswell Hill Junior School

DREAMER

Here is what my dreams contain,
Lots of joy and zero pain.
When I go
I do not know
Whether I'll want to return again.

Sitting in front of the TV
Waiting for the result of the lottery
Although it's a dream
I'm sure to gleam
Hearing my numbers, shouting *'Whoopee!'*
Floating through the deep, blue sky
Eating my favourite cherry pie
Seeing the stars
So near and far
Now on the sun I'll go and lie,
Lying there in a heavy sleep
Dreaming still in a pillow heap
Lying still, in my bed
Resting now my sleeping head
And at better dreams I now shall peep
With all of my might
Keep seeing the dream sight
But - it's time to wake
For goodness sake!
I'll be back next night!

Jason Bond (11)
Muswell Hill Junior School

THE HAUNTED HOUSE

Climbing up the creaky stairs,
Spiders hanging, watch out, *beware!*
There are spiders, spiders, everywhere,
It's like a really bad nightmare,
First stop is the billiard room,
This is where you're gonna meet your doom,
A bat flew past, mind out, *zoom!*
As I tiptoed in the moody gloom,
The last stop is the attic,
A place where your hair goes static,
There is an old hoover which is automatic,
I should use a quick tactic,
Run down the creepy stairs,
Oops! I've dropped my flares,
A ghost said 'Boo!' which gave me the scares,
I ran to the door and there were bears!

Aaahhhhhh!

Janine L Houston (10)
Muswell Hill Junior School

THE FAMOUS Q OF 007

Where would 007 be without
his gadgets, without the famous
Q of 007?

Cars, watches, guns, even mobiles,
gadgets made by the famous
Q of 007.

Akash Singh (9)
Muswell Hill Junior School

SILENCE

Silence sounds like whispers in the air,
Silence knows when not to be there,
Silence creeps like a lizard on his feet,
Silence is always there.
Silence keeps us on the edge of despair
It grows and grows until there is . . . nothing.

Silence is the push of a small animal
Silence is cold air rushing at your face.

Silence!

Kairos Pakleppa (11)
Muswell Hill Junior School

THE SUMMERTIME

Everybody loves the summertime
Having fun, having fun, having fun, in the summertime
Everybody loves the summertime
Folks get down in the summertime
Summertime, folks get brown in the summertime
Eating ice cream, drinking cool drinks,
            running around in the summertime
Butterflies, bees, trees and flowers come out in the summertime
Feeling hot, hot, hot in the summertime
How I love the summertime.

Dawn Duhaney (8)
Norfolk House School

SKI RUN

Snow, snow everywhere,
The fields are piled, the mountains too.
Icicles cage our wooden hut.
My little nose is blue.

Let's get moving, put on the skis.
Wrap up warmly, bend the knees.

I'm skiing down the long, long slope.
I see the end, I'm full of hope.
Now I'm like a ball of fire.
I'm steaming up. I'm not a liar.

Ben Kustow (11)
Norfolk House School

UP, UP AND AWAY IN MY AEROPLANE

In my aeroplane in the air,
I saw a flare from over there,
It was glowing fiery red
Went straight over my head,
And singed my long brown hair.

Gemma Mehmed (8)
Norfolk House School

FRIENDS

Friends are wonderful people to have
You can tell them all the troubles you have had.
Sometimes they're good, sometimes bad, but
Friends are not people that make you sad.
With friends you can meet up
Sometimes in a pub,
Friends are people who stick together
They are people who will stay forever,
Friends are such good people to have
They can make you very glad,
I am happy I have good friends
Without them I would be very sad.

George Surtees (10)
Norfolk House School

FLYING PIGS

Flying, flying, flying pigs
They're held up only by rigs
Up, up, up above
Flying, flying, like a dove
But they are not really flying
If they could, they would be
Lying, lying, lying.

Anna Bootle (8)
Norfolk House School

MOVING HOUSE

A huge great van, five big men
Knocked at our door one day
They carried all our belongings
Out and away.

They took my belongings where they didn't belong
And I cried because I thought it was wrong.
My clothes, my collections of gems and jewels
All went along with my Barbie's swimming pools.
My keyboards, my chest of drawers and my bed
Went to live somewhere else instead.

That night when I came home from school
We all had one last swim in our pool.
Then we climbed into Daddy's car
And Daddy said 'It won't be far.'

The house is smaller, there's not much space
And we do everything in terrible haste
The beds aren't made, the washing's not done
And everything is left up to Mum.

We've got a new bathroom
The kitchen comes this afternoon
I hope my bedroom gets decorated
Very, very soon.
I suppose when it's finished
I won't feel so alone
Then I can call the new house
'Home, sweet home!'

Afua Kokayi (8)
Norfolk House School

THE CAT

The cat crawled up the tree quietly,
Watching the bird hungrily,
We were watching the cat, my sister and me,
The bird saw the cat and just flew off the tree,
The bird flew round and round,
The cat looked for a chance to pounce,
I laughed and laughed,
My sister was tired
She wanted to go to bed,
So off she went leaving me alone,
Something was ringing,
It was her mobile phone.

The phone stopped ringing,
She missed her call,
The cat was fed-up,
It wanted to go home,
The bird flew off,
Leaving the cat alone.
The cat was thinking, 'How do I get down?'

I looked at its face,
I saw a little frown,
The cat was stuck,
Or so it seemed,
It miaowed and miaowed,
It wouldn't stop,
If it miaowed one more time I would go pop
Miaow
Bang!

Nicole Stennett (10)
Norfolk House School

HARVEST

Summer, autumn, winter, spring
The cycle of life is a wonderful thing.
The farmer sows the seeds in March,
When the soil is moist and dark.
The shoots begin to sprout in May.
In August time he makes the hay.
Next he gathers in the wheat.
Then fruit and veg are ready to eat.
Summer, autumn, winter, spring.
The cycle of life is a wonderful thing.

Sarah Grindall (10)
Osidge School

THE WISE CAT

Little cat up in the tree
Why are you staring down at me?
Is it because in your haste,
The next door's dog gave you chase
And you had no alternative
But to climb up high and sit and sit?
Perhaps little cat, I am mistaken
And whilst you sit silently in your haven,
You slyly plan your next meal,
When you eagerly hear the new chicks squeal.

Daniel Bezani (10)
Osidge School

THE DARK, DARK NIGHT

It was a dark, dark night
And I had a fright.
It was a creepy wood
And in a distance there it stood.
It was scary and hairy,
It had eyes that were bright,
What an awful sight!
I stood there shaking
And my heart was racing.
I ran out of that wood as fast as I could
And I can tell you now,
I will never go there again, never!

Kyri Neophytou (8)
Osidge School

THE WAVES

The waves soft, waves cold.
Blue, green see-through water and swim through
But only if I could have a beach in my room.

Waves can come in all different sorts of ways,
Waves can roar, waves can whisper, waves can jump.
Waves can run, waves can push, waves can brake sandcastles.

Waves can float like the sea of boats.
Waves are lovely to be in because of all the sorts of things they can do.

Vaishali Bhojani (8)
Osidge School

MYSTERIOUS SEA

Deep under water
Where no one dares to go
There are lots of life forms
Which no one will ever know.

As the owners whisk around
Lights are bobbing up and down
But no street lights are about
On the sandy ocean ground.

Scary spooky torchlights
Fill the ocean night
Are those creatures big or small?
Can you catch a sight?

Deep underwater
Where no one dares to go
There are lots of life forms
Which everyone now knows.

Zarrin Ansari (9)
Osidge School

ZOLA

My dream is to play with Zola
That skilful football star.
If I was as talented as him
I'm sure I would go far.

He has played for Napoli, Parma and Chelsea
And always been the best.
Although he's only five foot five
He's better than the rest!

Sean Shields (8)
Osidge School

CAKE

Soft, squidgy, hard or crispy,
I love you cake.

Round, square, triangle or rectangle,
I love you cake.

With custard, cream or chocolate sauce,
I love you cake.

Chewy, rough or hard to tear apart,
I love you cake.

Filled with buttercream, strawberry jam,
Or both of those.
I love you cake.

Cup cakes, tea cakes or fairy cakes,
I love you cake.

With icing on top,
I love you cake.

Chocolate cake or creamy cake,
I love you cake.

With cherries or strawberries on top,
I love you cake.

All sorts of cake,
I love you cake!

Danielle Davari (8)
Osidge School

THE SWIRLY OCEAN

The ocean rattles, tattles
All over the place.
There is a shark at the bottom of the ocean.
It is looking for its supper.
It is starving
It sees a goldfish
It opens its big jaws,
It grabs the goldfish and swallows it.
It is so tasty,
It finds fifty more little goldfish
It goes so black because the shark's jaws are going over the goldfish.
He munches them all up,
It is so tasty.
The shark goes back to sleep.
It snores and bubbles comes to the top of the ocean.
It is called the Pacific Ocean.

Alex Christodoulou (8)
Osidge School

THE FUNKY CHIPS

The funky chips go up and down
The funky chips are like lots of clowns.
The funky chips lied,
The funky chips died,
Because the funky chips got fried!

Harry Yard (8)
Osidge School

THE BLOB

The blob, the blob it's out,
The blob, the blob it's out.
The blob, the blob it's out.

It eats,
It squishes,
And it gobbles, gobbles, gobbles.

I quiver,
I shake
And I shiver, shiver, shiver.

All the people have been devoured.
It's coming for *me* in one hour!

The blob, the blob it-'s out.
The blob, the blob it's out.
The blob, the blob it's out.

I jumped up in mid-air.
Phew, it was only a nightmare!

Matthew Ridgley (8)
Osidge School

THE DEATH OF THE DINOSAURS

The death of the dinosaurs happened so quick
We don't know why, did they get sick?
Did they grow wings and fly away,
Flying around to this very day?
Did big mammals come and eat them up,
With soup and tea in a cup?
Did they hibernate for all these years,
Or feel so sad that they drowned in their tears?
If dinosaurs were here now, what would the Earth be like?
Would we be friends or would we fight?
One thing we know is they're not here anymore,
So that is that!
Maybe they'll come one day and ask for their bones back!

Elliot Savoie (11)
Pakeman Primary School

GARDENS

Tame the flowers, water the plants, trim the grass, plant more plants.
When it rains and it's dull and grey and you feel that you want to play,
Go out in the garden,
Have some fun you're bound to have something to do.

You can tame the flowers, water the plants,
Trim the grass, plant more plants.
That will be something to do.

When Mum says 'No' and Dad says 'Yes' and your brothers and sisters
are such pests.
Go out in the garden have some fun and again I say to you,
You can tame the flowers, water the plants, trim the grass, plant
more plants.
You never can say you've got nothing to do.

Kara Black (11)
Pakeman Primary School

THE TREE WHO WANTED TO MOVE

I'm big and grand and I stand very high,
But I want to move like all the creatures nearby.
I stand here alone all day long,
Waving my arms when the wind comes along,
I've been standing here for two hundred years,
The animals come by, here come some deers,
Oh how I want to move.

Eli Heller (10)
Pardes House Primary School

NATURE

Nature is fun,
To see how it works,
It looks so colourful,
Say thanks to Hashem.

Sruli Marks (10)
Pardes House Primary School

A HAIKU ON NATURE

Volcanoes, mountains,
Seas and all the animals
Hashem made them all.

Dovid Fulda (11)
Pardes House Primary School

NATURE

We make population,
From a bigger generation,
Seed, beans, plants, trees,
Sowing and growing pods with peas,
Seeds, beans, trees, flowers,
Growing between here and Alton Towers,
Garden and park,
Owl and lark,
Loads of plants keep growing
And also rivers overflowing,
Growing trees,
Dancing fleas,
Animals crying,
Seagulls flying
And to end
Rainbows blend.

Mordechai Teff (10)
Pardes House Primary School

WHEN THE WORLD WAS MADE

When the world was made,
Everything was in the right place,
People didn't have lice,
The trees were nice
And the countries were tidy,
The animals were gentle
And the sea wasn't rough,
Food was very good,
Water was fresh,
In the night the stars twinkled
And in the day the sun shined.

Ari Stimler (10)
Pardes House Primary School

WIND

Wind, wind, wind, wind,
It blows the kites that are flying high
And it blows the washing on the line,
It blows the clouds,
It blows the rain,
It blows the sea
And its waves.
It turns the cogs on windmills,
It blows up and down the grassy hills.
It blows the flowers in spring,
It makes the gliders fly
And sometimes you can hear it,
Rustling the leaves with a gentle sigh.

Mordechai Zeev Schwab (10)
Pardes House Primary School

NATURE

Nature is such a wonderful thing,
It makes all the plants living,
How all the things grow,
I really do not know,
All the birds sing,
At the time of spring,
On a summer's day,
We all play,
Life outside is as good as gold,
Even when it is really cold,
Because God made it.

Yitzchok Grunhut (11)
Pardes House Primary School

FRUIT

Apple, banana, orange, mango,
We eat them today, we eat them tomorrow.

Grapes, grapes, how do you grow?
We eat them today, we eat them tomorrow.

Pear, pear why are you green?
In my house you are always seen.

Orange, orange why are you orange?
I eat you every day but not with my porridge.

Cherries, plums, you are so red,
I like to eat you in my bed.

Hashem, Hashem you are so kind,
For giving us the food which we find.

Binyomin Burns (9)
Pardes House Primary School

MY BABY BROTHER

When my brother was born
I thought he was so sweet
By the look of his feet
For a very long time he couldn't walk
For a very long time he couldn't talk
But in the end he was able to walk and talk.
It was so wonderful to see him walk and
Hear him talk,
As he grew older he learnt more and more
And now he knows a very lot more.

Yehuda Heitner (9)
Pardes House Primary School

The Sky

The sun is bright
And it is very light.
The moon hides away
In the day.
When the moon comes out,
It comes out, at night
But unfortunately,
We don't get any light.
When the moon comes out
It is dark,
But it is a big shame
Because there is no lark.
Stars are very shiny
And they twinkle.
Rockets are big,
Rockets are long,
Rockets can come from Hong Kong.

Zvi Aisenthal (10)
Pardes House Primary School

Untitled

Hashem made the winter very nice
In the winter there is a lot of ice
The winter, the winter is no fun
But sometimes on the ice you can run.
Read a book in your house
And don't think of catching a mouse.
Here comes the summer full of flowers
All bright, full of colours.

Meir Chaim Sellam (10)
Pardes House Primary School

OH WHAT A WONDERFUL WORLD

Oh trees and bushes how beautiful you are,
It's a pity so many things can harm you like fumes from a car.

Oh shimmering sea and bubbling brook,
How clear and sparkling your waters look.

Oh grass and shrubs how nice is your coat green,
Never has a nicer sight ever been seen.

Oh how fertile you look, green and brown soil,
Believe me, to all your plants you're very loyal.

Oh how splendid you are when you twinkle, my dear stars
And how I love to smell you, red roses in a vase.

Oh how magnificent you look with your colours, rainbow,
Red, orange, yellow, green, blue and indigo.

Oh how glistening you look, rain, so gentle and so clear,
The constant pitter-pattering is so nice to hear.

Oh how soft you look, clouds, so fluffy and white,
You truly are the greatest sight.

Oh weather whatever you send,
Be it rain, snow or sun I'll always be your friend.

Oh with what a wonderful world we've been blessed,
Enjoy each day and live with zest.

Dovid Atlas (10)
Pardes House Primary School

SNOW

The snow had fallen in the night
And the temperature was just right,
The snow had settled six inches high
And the kids danced as the snow fell from the sky.

There were snowballs flying everywhere,
A snowman sitting on the headmaster's chair,
Children yelling at the top of their voices,
Cars at a standstill, even some Rolls Royce's.

Girls were skipping in the snow,
Boys passing the ball in a row,
Teachers trying to keep the classroom neat,
Parents trying to brush snow off their feet.

Then all of a sudden rain began to fall,
Everyone ran into the school hall,
The teacher gave a long assembly
And the children sat waiting impatiently.

Finally when they got back into daylight,
To their dismay, a terrible sight,
The snow had all melted by the warm rain
And all the children watched as it disappeared down the drain.

Yehuda Diamant (10)
Pardes House Primary School

DAYS OF THE WEEK

I am the seventh day
Hashem rested this day
He finished creating the world
On this day
Everything was in the world
Everything that needed to be
From elephants to bees
What day am I?

Hashem created fish
Birds and water creatures
From ants to elephants
He created something by the sand
Which is the sea.

Hashem made the first man
The first lady and
The first of all the animals
And the man was named Adam.

Shloimie Hammer (10)
Pardes House Primary School

THE SEASONS

In spring it is nice and cool
But it can also be hot,
If in the evening it is not cold,
You can have a barbecue beside a pot. (Outside)

In the summer we go to the beach
And we eat cold things like frozen peach.
We eat ice lollies and ice-cream
We stick our feet into a freezing stream.

In the autumn down comes the leaves
And then we see all the bare trees,
It starts to get cool
But from that cold you cannot freeze.

In the winter down comes the snow
And the snow is cold, as you know,
The children play outside on sledges
And smash into farm hedges.

Motti Wiesenfeld (10)
Pardes House Primary School

NATURE

Nature is something made by Hashem
And is really pleasant
To smell or look at
Use or make it
Really it's pleasant
Everything is made by Hashem.

It looks nice
So why not smell it.

Nothing is square
And nothing is man-made
The wood and trees
Up away they go in fire
Really a waste
And I'm really upset to
Let them go away.

Binyomin Weissbraun (11)
Pardes House Primary School

THE RAINFOREST

Are one the earth and sky,
Just like you and I,
As the macaw and dove fly up above,
The monkeys sing with love,
While the cheetah runs,
A special bird hums,
When the fox picks his meal,
All the rabbits squeal,
Please don't pick me,
They squeak hee, hee,
With their fur so white,
Oh my!
What a sight
And the giraffe so tall,
A poor skunk so small,
When the jaguars stalk,
Flying is the hawk
And the rainbow so high,
Shining brightly in the sky.

Eliyohu Hye (10)
Pardes House Primary School

AUTUMN

Reds, oranges, browns and greens
The autumn leaves fall off the trees.
Whoosh, swoosh a big breeze
Blows away a number of leaves
The hedgehogs should hurry to hibernate
Before it becomes too late
The rain falls and feeds the flowers
Soon we'll play in the sun for hours and hours.
Most of the children start school
While the weather is becoming cool
Hats and scarves and all the rest
And don't forget your woolly vest!
The squirrels collect plenty of nuts
And hide them behind the garden huts.
When spring approaches I've got plenty of plans
Like running around then drinking cans.

Mordechai Cutler (10)
Pardes House Primary School

THE WONDERS OF THE SKY

'What colour is the sky?'
The sky is white that is the colour of the sky.
'Where does the sky live?'
The sky lives up there high up,
Where the stars are
And the moon and sun,
Have their peaceful rest,
'I can't see the moon anywhere,
The moon for the moment is not there,
It is only there when it is dark.'

Mordechai Katzenberg (9)
Pardes House Primary School

NATURE

There are two types of *nature,*
One, the character of any creature.
For example, Tzvi is rather crafty
And Chananya is rather nasty
And it is the second type of *nature,*
The body of any creature.
For example, who made the tree,
Or who made the buzzing bee?
All those answers are *nature*
And for it to remember, think of a creature.

Nature is natural, most things are from *nature.*
All the many kinds of a creature.
The trees, the plants and the flower
United in an again *nature* rain shower!
Remember even you and I are *nature*
Endless is the thing for that word
Nature.

Sruli Lerner (11)
Pardes House Primary School

NATURE

Nature about animals
Animals are cute
Tigers are vicious
We are happy when Hashem makes it
Reptiles and snakes are cool,
End of animals nature.

Pets are nice to keep
Of fun and games
End of pet nature
Mammals are the ones that don't lay eggs.

Dovid Gluck
Pardes House Primary School

ANIMALS

Have you ever seen a dog that hops like a frog?
Have you ever seen a cat who jumps in a hat?
Have you ever seen a goat with a red coat?
Have you ever seen a fish make a wish?
Have you ever seen a rabbit that has a bad habit?
Have you ever seen a monkey riding on a donkey?
Have you ever seen a mouse that picked a house?
Have you ever seen a pig who had a wig?
Have you ever seen a fish swim in a dish?
Have you ever seen a shark play in a park?

Cavell Robert Nuamah (9)
St Francis De Sales Junior School

TRENDY TEACH

Our teacher's really trendy,
She wears real cool clothes.

Our teacher's really trendy,
She never ever moans.

Our teacher's really trendy,
She's got platforms for every day.

Our teacher's really trendy
And cool in every way.

Our teacher's really trendy,
She's only 23, (Oops!)

Our teacher's really trendy,
Can't you see?

Our teacher's really trendy,
So there's no need to fear,

Our teacher's really trendy,
'Cause you'll have her
Next year!

Sinead Clinton (9)
St Francis De Sales Junior School

ANIMALS

I like animals,
I think they're really cool,
I have a favourite animal,
It is a house mouse,
Where they meet lots of louse.
I also have another one,
It is a forest bear,
Even though they give you quite a scare!
I have a pet dog
He's quite a cute one,
Although he spoils our fun, (My sister and I)
I almost forgot to mention,
I like the Akkard wolf,
Because they're really tiny and cute.
So there you have it,
It's so plain to see,
That I want is to be a vet when I'm older,
Just you wait and see!

Róisín Intavarant (10)
St Francis De Sales Junior School

MY DAD

My dad is small,
Not tall at all,
He is not in fashion!
He has black hair with specks of grey.
My dad's face is as red as a rose,
He has a bushy moustache.

Carla McGrath (9)
St Francis De Sales Junior School

IN THE PLAYGROUND I CAN SEE

In the playground I can see
Susie sings,
Liam laughs,
Fred fights,
Reyzil runs,
Daniel dances,
Billy bounces,
Cavell cries,
Shazzy shakes and
Laura leaps.

Deanna Mary-Jane Williams (9)
St Francis De Sales Junior School

VALENTINE'S DAY

One Valentine's Day
Love is in the air
Love flows in February
Love is like long flowing hair.

Love flows everywhere,
Your heart is like gold,
You care about everybody
It doesn't matter if you're young or old.

Charlotte O'Brien (8)
St Francis De Sales Junior School

ANIMALS

A dog is a man's best friend,
A cat goes round the bend,
A fish swims round and round,
A parrot flies above the ground,
A bear is very big.
A monkey hangs onto a twig,
A shark has big jaws,
A cub licks its paws,
A cheetah runs so fast,
A turtle has such a task,
A gorilla is very tough,
A leopard is very rough.

Craig Kirkton (8)
St Francis De Sales Junior School

MY DAD

My dad is short
But he has a lot of thought.
My dad is plump
But he's not a frump.
My dad is funny
He calls me Honey.
My dad is happy
He says I'm yappy.
He dresses smart
He's got a kind, kind heart.

Cally Browne (8)
St Francis De Sales Junior School

THE PLAYGROUND

The playground is a big noisy space
With children running all over the place,
With rings and balls and teacher's face,
Trying to keep up with the pace.

There's Tracie and Theresa and then Mrs Peck
Trying their hardest to keep us in check,
All the boys and girls that play,
Come rain or shine day after day.

'Line up!' they shout. 'Don't shove and push.'
But one child away ends up in a bush.
Now Mr McBride says 'Come, get in line'
Everyone rushes to be in time,
Trying to hide the smiles on their face
As our teachers lead us from the big, noisy space.

Paul Hardy (10)
St Francis De Sales Junior School

THE YEAR 2000

The year 2000 has come
Let's hope the year is a good one
With peace and love throughout the world.
Where people care and lend a hand
And try to help and understand.
All in all I'd like to say the year 2000 has come to stay.

Carmel Fernandes (9)
St Francis De Sales Junior School

THE ARTIST

The lines she drew were dark
The brush was beautiful and sharp
She handled the strokes with grace and air,
The details were added with care.

The colours were sparing yet vibrant
She created a certain glow
Only she would know,
She looked up with excitement.

The contours of her face,
Were enhanced with a chase
With her lipstick she added a seal of embrace.

Melanie Socrates (9)
St Francis De Sales Junior School

MY GRANDAD

My grandad is plump and short,
He has grey hair and likes to watch sport.
He wears square glasses and he is old,
He has bushy hair and he's always cold.
He wears lots of old fashioned things
And he sounds so dreadful when he sings.
He plays the piano really cool
And he's always talking about his days at school.

Rachel Smethers (8)
St Francis De Sales Junior School

AS FAST AS SLOW

As fast as a cheetah,
As slow as a turtle.
As fast as a motorbike,
As slow as a ladybird.
As fast as a car,
As slow as a boat.
As fast as an aeroplane,
As slow as an ant.
As fast as a dog,
As slow as a mouse.
As fast as a rollerblade,
As slow as a bird.
As fast as a bike.

Nneamaka Jessica Ijeh (8)
St Francis De Sales Junior School

METAPHOR

The sun is a big, round, burning ball,
The moon is a big, round, silver ball.
School is a prison for kids,
A car is a monster with sharp teeth and big, round eyes.
Thunder is a crowd of people shouting at a match.
The stars are shiny flashing lights.
The rain is a tear falling from the sky,
Night is a total eclipse.
Lightning is an electric shock coming towards you.

Angela Asiaw (8)
St Francis De Sales Junior School

My Hungry Cat

I have a black cat
Who is very fat.
She wanted juicy mice,
That tasted rather nice.
She chased the mice,
Like a little rolling dice,
Then went to bed
And looked well fed.

My cat is called Sheila,
Her favourite food's Sheba.
She swallows her food,
In a very good mood,
Then finishes late
And licks her plate.
She cleans herself all over,
As I refill her bowl with sparkling water!

Sheila likes to eat fresh fish,
I gave her one and she cleaned the dish,
There were six more lying on the floor
And she looked at me for some more.
I thought about it then gave her two,
She started to swallow and started to chew,
So she finished her fish and though she's fat,
I don't mind and neither does my cat!

Winnie Rebello (10)
St Francis De Sales Junior School

MY SIMILE POEM

As fast as a cheetah,
As slow as a turtle.
As soft as a sock,
As small as an ant.
As big as an elephant,
As sharp as a knife.
As dull as mud,
As shining as the sun.
As red as blood,
As blue as the sky.
As loud as a dog,
As hungry as a lion.
As funny as a clown,
As fun as a bouncy castle.
As sweet as sugar,
As dry as a desert
And as deep as a river.

Desmond Hammond (9)
St Francis De Sales Junior School

GHOST GIRL

I saw a ghost girl watching me
On the rooftops never breathing
Never moving only watching.

I saw a ghost girl watching me
The spookiest feelings over me,
So creepy and so very scary.

I saw a ghost girl watching me,
Never twitching, never blinking
Only watching, barely smiling.

And very slowly, drifting nearer
White and see through
Coming closer
To the window, through the glass.

Ricardo Garcia De Paredes (10)
St Francis De Sales Junior School

THE ANGEL AND DEVIL

I'm an angel when I'm at school,
But when I come out you should see the things I do,
I run, I scream, I jump about
And this is only the end of part one but tighten
Your seat belt, it's only just begun . . .

Now I'm in school, the ring is around my head,
They all say, 'What a wonderful kid'
'Huh, huh, huh, huh, they know nothing,'
The things I do, the things I say, every single minute
Of the day.
Of course not on school days,
Because remember I'm an angel.
This is the end of part two but always remember
The things I do,
Because I may inspire you.
Anyway I have things to do,
Why not be mischievous and do the things I do,
But remember in school the angel is due . . .

Sara Adusei (9)
St Francis De Sales Junior School

THE YEAR 2000

When it comes the special year
Everybody starts to cheer
Waiting for the millennium to come
Everybody's having fun!

Shouting and drinking
Talking and thinking
Everybody's singing
And are happy with glee.

Happy millennium! They shout hooray
This has been a happy day.

Now it is the special year
Everybody starts to cheer
Now the millennium has come
Everybody's having fun!

Jessica Dixon (11)
St Francis De Sales Junior School

TREES

Green trees in winter
Some trees are green all year round
Beautiful green trees.

Lucy McGinn (8)
St Francis De Sales Junior School

SUMMERTIME

I love coconuts
I drink them on dolphins' backs
Bees hover about.

Kiara Louise Duffy (8)
St Francis De Sales Junior School

IN THE CLASSROOM

The children work hard
They work as hard as they can
But talk very loud.

Demi Flynn (7)
St Francis De Sales Junior School

WET WEATHER

Rain is dropping down
Hailstones are now tearing down
Drip, drop, drip, drop, drip.

Amy O'Leary (7)
St Francis De Sales Junior School

WEATHER

The rain is sploshing,
The hailstones are falling down,
On the slippery floor.

Chisom Diorgu (8)
St Francis De Sales Junior School

WET WEATHER

Umbrellas go up
Keep it up because there's rain
There must be a storm.

Leanne Cronin (7)
St Francis De Sales Junior School

RAINBOW

The rainbow is bright,
The rainbow is colourful
A magic rainbow.

Tanya Louise Williams (7)
St Francis De Sales Junior School

SUMMERTIME

Swimming in the sea
Dancing children, I love them
Joyful days they were.

Katie Ronan (8)
St Francis De Sales Junior School

WET WEATHER

The rain is dropping
The rain is dropping down hard
The sky is cloudy.

Hilda Asiaw (7)
St Francis De Sales Junior School

PARTY

I wear nail polish,
I wear blusher and glitter,
We dance with the boys

Naomi Nicholson (7)
St Francis De Sales Junior School

CATS

Cats are cute and fun,
I am getting one today,
I am excited.

Charlie Winslow (7)
St Francis De Sales Junior School

CLOCK

Tick-tock, tick-tock, tick,
What's the time on the clock, nine
That's OK, that's fine.

Laura Malone (7)
St Francis De Sales Junior School

MY FAMILY

My dad is fun, fit and strong
On the other hand, my brother gets things wrong.

My sisters are okay
But when they hit me, it's time to pay!

My auntie and mum are number one,
They give me love as bright as the sun.

Frederick Oppong (9)
St Francis De Sales Junior School

MUM'S ORDERS!

Brush your teeth,
Comb your hair,
Before you go outside,
Wash the dishes,
Feed the fishes,
Before you go to bed.
Get your shoes and put them on,
Then please walk the dog.
Make sure things are put away,
Then please feed the frog.
It's your sister's birthday party,
So blow up some balloons.
But hurry up because dinner is very soon.
Oh no! She's now coming back from the hair saloon!

Bernice John-Cave (11)
St Ignatius RC Primary School

CELEBRATIONS

Celebrations enlighten
The world,
Magical lights embrace
The night sky,
Birthdays make life
More beautiful,
Anniversaries lighten
The days,
Invitations open
All occasions
Everyone praise celebrations.

Matthew Henderson (10)
St Ignatius RC Primary School

MILLENNIUM 2000

M is for millennium which are celebrated every 1000 years,
I is for intelligent people who celebrated the millennium with us.
L is for lovely people who celebrated celebrations with us.
L is for light which is shown at celebrations.
E is for enjoyment that we have at celebrations.
N is for nice gifts with lovely things inside.
N is for near places where we celebrate the millennium,
I is for immediate people who come to the millennium,
U is for united people you celebrate with us,
M is for mothers who celebrate with us.

Bob Maxwell Akanga Lincoln (10)
St Ignatius RC Primary School

CELEBRATIONS

Celebrations, celebrations,
We like celebrations,
Birthday parties,
Christmas parties,
We like celebrations,
It may be a wedding day,
It may be an engagement day,
It may be a Valentine day,
Celebrations, celebrations,
We like celebrations,
If there were no celebrations,
Everyone would have devastation,
They would stamp their feet,
Shout out loud
Fight with each other
Quarrel with each other.

Davina Joshua (10)
St Ignatius RC Primary School

ORANGES AND SNOW

The smell and colour of oranges stood in front of the pale snow,
Silently, the snow was sliding onto the hard streets of the night.
The moist oranges were disappearing under a sheet of ice.
The hard skin was fading into frost, until the snow started to melt,
Releasing the beauty of summer again.

Patrick Raimondi Taylor (10)
St Ignatius RC Primary School

SIR

As I was coming to school, sir,
To learn my ABC,
I was picked up and put in a sack, sir
And carried off on his back, sir,
By my MP who took me to sea,
So I had to swim all the way back, sir
And I still had my legs in the sack, sir
And the waves were forty foot high, sir,
Which is the reason why, sir,
I would not tell a lie, sir,
I am a bit late for school, sir!

Samantha Judge (11)
St Ignatius RC Primary School

SEASON OF THE LEAVES

Autumn cold, autumn dark,
All the leaves fall to the ground,
All the leaves are yellow and brown
And then they swirl all round and round.

The harvest is collected
And the squirrels are protected
From the bitter autumn
Hallowe'en was last night but I wasn't scared at all,
Now I shiver with the cold as the leaves fall down.

Autumn!

Fiona Harkin (10)
St Ignatius RC Primary School

PREDATORS

Predators, predators are alligators and boa constrictors,
Think teeth, think claws, think clamping jaws,
You'll be extinct in a blink of an eye,
Birds even plants sleeping at day, hunting at night,
Hawks from the skies are very fly,
They are fast with their wings,
They catch a lot of things,
Plants make traps for flies from the skies,
A cat like a bat is a predator,
Think of the cat roaming around the house eating mice,
Cheetahs, cheetahs, are also meat eaters,
Predators can be big, predators can be small,
Horrifying blood shines all on the walls,
Snakes are venomous, eating prey in one big munch,
Dogs munch in a bunch,
Always together, hunting with each other,
Slashing and clashing, smashing and crashing,
Crunching bones, hurtful, groans,
Munching meat, just for them to eat.

Lloyd Marfo (10)
St Ignatius RC Primary School

TELEVISION

I watch TV and go up close
Of course my eyesight, yes I know
Away from it I may not go
Moesha, MTV, Pokémon too,
When they are on at the same time
I don't know what to do
I watch TV and go up close
Away from it, I may not go.

Atinuke Odunsi (10)
St Ignatius RC Primary School

LET'S HAVE FUN

Let's have fun and enjoy ourselves,
Presents are put on the living room shelves,
Sweets, candy, doughnuts and scrumptious popcorn,
People dancing all day long,
The colourful candles are put on the icing,
The birthday boy or girl will start dancing,
The games we play give the greatness of the party,
Everyone feels extremely hearty,
Children and adults, mouths shaped like fruit slices,
Children play pass the parcel and win prizes,
That is how a merry party is celebrated,
With great happiness and is appreciated.

Marie Amoateng (11)
St Ignatius RC Primary School

MY LOVE FOR YOU

My love for you is higher than the sky,
My love for you rises with the morning sun,
My love began with a seed which was placed
                              in my heart,
My perfect love,
My perfect day,
Your tender lips touch mine with a sparkle,
Your deep blue eyes are washed up along the shore,
I love your cuddles when your arms are around me.

Christine James (10)
St Ignatius RC Primary School

THE MOUSE WHO NEVER WENT AWAY

There was a man who lived in a house,
but was always troubled by a mouse.
When one died, another one came
which soon made the man become insane.

When the fridge is opened and there is no cheese there,
you know mice have been around here.
The man called the exterminator, what could he do?
Keep breathing up dust from the floor and catch the 'flu.

The man decided he couldn't take it and said 'No more,'
Packed all his bags, walked out of the house and slammed the door.
He moved away from there to a new house
and you'll never guess what he saw in there, he saw a mouse.

Oluseun Oniyide (11)
St Ignatius RC Primary School

WHAT SHALL HAPPEN IN THE FANTASY WORLD IN THE NEW MILLENNIUM?

What shall happen in the fantasy world?
The unicorn's horn will be shimmering like the sea
And the fairies will be wearing leopard skin bikinis.
Pegasus's wings will lead him into the heavens
And the fawn will be as playful as a child,
But Santa will be begging children to give him presents.
But I have news that is much worse,
Which actually sounds more like a curse.
The witches won't stop being too kind, like pests,
When Dorothy came and slapped them on the hind and all the rest.

Louise McHugh (10)
St Ignatius RC Primary School

MY POEM ABOUT FOOTBALL

Football is fun for everyone.
Once you play it is so much fun.
When the whistle starts to blow
The crowd goes 'Wahoo, let's go!'
When the crowd sees a foul,
All you can hear is a big howl.
When a goal is scored, no one gets bored,
They all get up and roar.
When this happens I cover my ears
And then get down on the floor,
So from now on, I stay at home
And watch it on the telly,
But even then I still have my brothers to disturb me.

Daniel Opoku Akwaboa (11)
St Ignatius RC Primary School

A POEM ON CELEBRATIONS AND WITHOUT CELEBRATION

Without celebrations we can't grant congratulations,
Without celebrations we can't sing to our nation,
A celebration is a time when we get together for an occasion,
It will be a shame to miss out on the occasion
With one another, or with our brother.
We sing, we bring sometimes a wedding ring.

Just think!
Without celebrations,
We will never have a chance to say
'Congratulations!'

Karl Heron (10)
St Ignatius RC Primary School

A World Without Celebrations

Celebrations, celebrations, I like celebrations.
Imagine a world without celebrations,
There would be no need to send information on invitations.

Without celebrations the world will be filled with different devastations
It would be so boring that everyone would
Have no choice but to start roaring.
There'd be so much pain that
All people will go insane.
No parties, nor gathering when battles are won,
Children will run
Because they have no fun.

Celebrations, celebrations, without them we cannot
Celebrate the great people of our nations,
So always remember, we need celebrations.

Stephen Amode (11)
St Ignatius RC Primary School

What Kind Of Pokémon Are You?

What kind of Pokémon are you?
How do you do the things you do?
Are you a normal type like Jigglypuff
Or a ghastly Gengar who battles real tough?

From rock to fire, Machamp can use Choke,
Use Squirtle on Charmander, his tail goes up in smoke.
Colourless, water, don't forget lightning,
Get all the energy and it becomes frightening.

Reece Lambert (8)
St John The Evangelist RC Primary School

I Want To Be A Pop Star

I want to be a pop star,
I want to be it now,
If I can't be a pop star,
I'll stamp and scream and howl.
I want to be a pop star now, now, now,
I want to be a pop star,
I want to be it now.
I want to dance on stage and sing
And do the funky tango.
What could my name be, what? What? What?
I want to be a pop star,
I want to be a pop star,
I want to be it now!

Laura McAteer (8)
St John The Evangelist RC Primary School

The Old Man U

Home or away,
We're always there when they play,
We're the lads that back the team,
Standing on the terraces is my dream

We are the old Man U,
If you want to play we'll beat you,
Because football is our game
And Man U is our name.

Josh St John (9)
St John The Evangelist RC Primary School

I Have A Dog Called Muk

I have a dog called Muk
He always gives me luck.
He's always in the mud
And when he is, he gets a big thud.

Blood red is his favourite colour,
He almost bit my mother.
He hates my brother very much
Or any stranger that gives him a touch.

I love Muk
he gives me luck
But when he's in the mud
I just have to give him a thud.

So bye now
Don't get a frown
I'll be back soon
Well at least not on the moon.

Aston Alefounder (10)
St John The Evangelist RC Primary School

A Winter's Day

The winter is cold and dark,
But I still ask Mummy
'Can I go round to the park?'
I hope it snows on the slide,
To make a really good ride.

Sarah Kee (8)
St John The Evangelist RC Primary School

WORLD WAR TWO

W ar breaking out
O ur troops are at the ready
R unning from the bombs
L ondon hit!
D own the bomb shelters.

W omen and children are evacuated.
A ir raids sounding
R unning from death.

T oday we would like
W orld peace
O ver and everywhere with everyone.

Ryan Bennett (11)
St John The Evangelist RC Primary School

SUMMER FUN

Children screaming, having fun,
Playing games, eating ice-cream,
Swimming in lanes,
Mothers calling them for tea,
Then they can come and play with me.
Now we're playing hide-and-seek,
It is my turn to count,
But I promise not to peek.
Another day is over and gone,
But tomorrow we'll have lots more fun.

Sinead Finn (8)
St John The Evangelist RC Primary School

LIEUTENANT MAJOR

Lieutenant Major Lunacy Fool
Bought an old mansion complete with a ghoul.
He tried to get rid of it as fast as he could,
But an old lady came and said that she should.

This old lady she tried and tried,
But the ghoul always managed to hide.
Then the lady said to the major,
'I quit, look here's back your pager.'

Then the lady walked out the door,
And the ghoul came right through the floor.
'Boo, I'm your spectre!' he shouted.
When Fool saw the ghoul he doubted.

When the ghoul saw his face,
He floated right below his lace,
He came back up through the floor,
And then he shot right out the door.

That is the story of Lieutenant Fool,
Who never again saw the ghoul at all.

Chad McCamlie (10)
St John The Evangelist RC Primary School

UP AND DOWN

Up and down
Is a funny town,
Where folk stand on their heads
And believe it or not they don't sleep in beds!
All the girls there are called Jess and boys are called Jay
And at school they start their alphabet with a Z and end it with an A.

Sade Ali (8)
St John The Evangelist RC Primary School

MY SPECIAL STAR

There is a star in the sky
So very, very high.
I watch it every night
Shine its twinkling light.

I know it watches down on me,
Keeps me safe and full of glee.
I sometimes even talk to it
When it's the only star lit.

We talk about how our day has been
And what interesting things we had seen.
Its day is in the night
And mine is in the light.

I am very sad when it has to go
As I watch all light go low.
I'm really glad I know the star
Up in the sky so very far.

Mary-Grace Sturley (10)
St John The Evangelist RC Primary School

MY DAD

My dad was such fun but now he's dead.
These are some of my memories:
My dad was big
But he was fun.
My dad called me Princess
But he only took me to places of fun.
My dad, my dad so handsome, so handsome.

Jordan Alefounder (9)
St John The Evangelist RC Primary School

COLONEL FAZACKERLY

Colonel Fazackerly Butterworth Coast
Bought an old cottage with a ghost
But someone or other forgot to declare
That Colonel Fazackerly should 'beware'.

On the very first evening, while waiting to dine
The colonel was having a fine strawberry wine.
Then with a flash and very bright flare.
The colonel found out a spectre was there.

'I fought in the war and I was shot in the head,
When a beautiful lady found out I was dead.'
Colonel Fazackerly shouted, 'Encore.
Give me more, give me more!'

Without a doubt the spectre had left
When out strolled the chef, 'Lunch is served.'
Colonel Fazackerly finally went to dine
Enjoying his fine strawberry wine.

Kieron Fensome-Deane (10)
St John The Evangelist RC Primary School

MY SISTER

She mumbles and grumbles,
She moans and groans,
She yells and smells,
But she can smile for a while.

She wriggles and giggles,
She shouts about.
She burps and slurps,
But I love her, because I'm her big brother.

Alex James (9)
St John The Evangelist RC Primary School

SANDY

Sandy was my fluffy friend
Sandy was my mate
I took her for walks every day
She never ran far away
We played together every day
No matter what the weather
Sandy was quite an old dog
She had a happy life
Then one day when I came home from school
Sandy was not in sight
Sandy, Sandy, Sandy I cried
My mum walked in the room
When I saw her face I knew
Sandy had died
Every day I dream of her
And wipe away a tear
But in my dreams Sandy my friend
Will always be with me.

Emma Collins (8)
St John The Evangelist RC Primary School

THE INVENTOR'S WORKSHOP

In the inventor's workshop you can hear:
Buttons bleeping like a mad microwave.
You can see a computer as big as an elephant.
You can smell smoke and coffee from when the inventor takes a break.
The shelves are full of jars and boxes,
The films in the drawers are all tangled up,
Chemistry sets are all over the wall
So the inventor can make chemicals.

David Fox (9)
St John The Evangelist RC Primary School

HOLIDAYS

Mum packs the suitcases,
We pack our rucksack,
We're going on holiday to the sunshine.
Goodbye to the rain and cold.
Dad has the tickets,
We all wait at the airport.
We are off again
Where the sea is blue,
Away for three weeks.
We get into our hotel
And see our rooms.
We change into summer clothes
And walk to the swimming pool.
Everybody's swimming in the clear water.
Lots of sun cream on my skin.
Plenty of water for me to swim.
Sand and sandcastles and ice-creams
This is the holiday of my dreams.

Edward Davis (8)
St John The Evangelist RC Primary School

THE CAT

There was a little cat,
He lived in a house,
He wiggled his tail,
Just like a mouse.

He sneaked by a tree,
He snaked by a pig,
He sneaked by a cow
And he sneaked by me.

He miaowed at a duck,
He miaowed at a rat,
He miaowed at a tree
But he pulled a face at me.

He stalked by a rabbit,
He stalked by a squirrel,
He stalked by a tree
And he stalked by me.

Ashley Savastano (6)
St John The Evangelist RC Primary School

THE PEOPLE UPSTAIRS

The people upstairs are very loud
Their voices are like big thunder clouds.

They invite people all day,
And it's really, really not OK.

When they bathe the floor creaks,
The water drips down and the ceiling leaks.

It's really quiet when they are out,
Nobody talks and nobody shouts.

I think the ceiling's going to crack,
If those people upstairs never pack.

I really like the people up there,
But sometimes they just give you a scare.

Rashid Nuku (9)
St John The Evangelist RC Primary School

THE ANIMAL HOUSE

As I walked into the black dark basement,
Howling sounds of wolves
I could hear.
Squeaky, squirmy snakes
Ugly fearing rats and
Dark black bats
And Koala bears.
I can't say much about my basement, my bedroom's worse.
Monkeys swinging from light to light,
Lions resting on the bed.
Crocodiles wrestling elephants.
Hare and tortoise racing.
Bear just make noise.
Wait take a look at the kitchen.
Cats in the fridge,
Fish in the sink.
Iguanas taking over the hob.
Rabbits acting cool
Birds singing
I'm lucky the animals are not taking over the living room
'Oh no, eagle!'
Guess what?
Poo on the door!

Giuseppe Capillo (8)
St John The Evangelist RC Primary School

THE WITCH'S KITCHEN

The shelves are dusty as an old carpet
The grandfather clock on the wall is stuck on twelve.
There are no sounds
Except the bubbles of the cauldron.
The creaking of the floorboards as the witch hobbles about.
The top of the witch's hat hangs on the wall.
The table's three legs are shaped like horses' bones.
The witch never throws her old things away.
She never put them in the garbage.
Indeed, she keeps them and throws them in her cauldron.
The air is full of cat litter
The grandfather clock has stopped at twelve
She stands for hours
Wondering what she is going to make
For her next potion.

Gerald Slattery (9)
St John The Evangelist RC Primary School

DOWN BY THE DUSTBIN

Down by the dustbin
Stanley met a rabbit.
It was hopping around
As it looked for a carrot.

Down by the dustbin
Stanley met a frog.
It was hopping around
As it looked at the fog.

Joseph Woods-McConville-Taylor (6)
St John The Evangelist RC Primary School

THE WITCH'S KITCHEN

The shelves are as dusty as old carpet.
The grandfather clock on the wall is stuck on twelve.
There are no sounds except the bubbles from the cauldron
    and the creaking floorboards, as the witch hobbles about.
The cone of the witch's hat hangs on the wall.
The table's legs are shaped like horse bones.
The witch never throws her old things away.
She never puts them in the garbage.
Indeed, she keeps them and throws them in the cauldron.
The air is full of the smell of cat litter.
The grandfather clock has stopped at twelve.
She stands for hours by her cat
And wondering what she is going to do for her new potion.

Aishling Quinn (9)
St John The Evangelist RC Primary School

THE WITCH'S KITCHEN

The cupboards are as dusty
As an old musty book.
The cauldron is filled with rats and bats.
It smells like potions have dropped all over the floor.
You can hear the witch screaming with lots of joy,
She just made a new potion.
Then she accidentally dropped it all over the floor.
She got a bit mad.
The potion took eleven years to make.

Harry Balding (9)
St John The Evangelist RC Primary School

THE PEOPLE UPSTAIRS

The people upstairs are crazy,
They can be a little lazy.

The people upstairs never read,
Instead they sit and play with beads.

The people upstairs get so many letter,
The trouble is they're always ill, 'So please get better!'

The people upstairs are always sitting down,
They think they're queens wearing their crowns.

The people upstairs never get on,
I'm surprised not one of them has gone.

The people like to have laughs,
The trouble is they can't get out of the bath.

The people upstairs have got so many pets,
And they are always putting on bets.

The people upstairs always shout,
So I phoned the police, they said, 'There's nothing to worry about!'

Jade Blackmore (9)
St John The Evangelist RC Primary School

DOWN BY THE DUSTBIN

Down by the dustbin
Stanley met a bat.
It was flapping its wings
As it waited for a rat.

Down by the dustbin
Stanley met a snake.
It was slithering around
As it waited for a cake.

Philippa Jane Davis
St John The Evangelist RC Primary School

THE SEA

I think the sea is a wonderful thing.
I like to watch it move.
I like to lie down in the calm sea.
I like to float on the sea and dream wonderful dreams.
I like to lie down by the sea and listen to the sea float,
                        like being poured into a cup.
I like to imagine I am in a waterbed dreaming a wonderful dream.
I also like the rough sea on a lovely sunny day.
I like to play games, pretending I am on a secret mission.
I like to imagine I'm surfing on gigantic waves,
                        having the time of my life.

Sean Parsons (9)
St Martin Of Porres RC Primary School

THE LION

The lion is a violent, dangerous man-eating creature,
He has a nice innocent look with his nice shaggy, furry coat,
But inside he is more or less a vicious monster of pride.

His wife is also very vicious.
Just because she has to take care of the cubs
It doesn't mean she can't be violent.

By the time the family get to their homes
The lion takes his sunken teeth out of his prey.
You look at him and you see his razor-sharp, lethal, blood-
                                    covered teeth.

I think you would be quite stunned if you dare to go and see
                                    this creature!

Bobo Ahmed (10)
St Martin Of Porres RC Primary School

THE WAVY SEA

The sea is nice, the sea is beautiful,
The sea has fish which are so exotic.
The sea has dreams it is so calm,
The sea is cold the waves are gold
And the sunlight shines on the wavy sea.
The sea has wonders and is full of memories.
The sea is soft, I don't know why,
When I go into the ocean I am so warm.
The sea is sleepy and blue and very silky.

Kathryn O'Donoghue (8)
St Martin Of Porres RC Primary School

THE ANGRY SEA

The waves are crashing,
The sea is roaring,
It feels freezing.
The current is pounding,
The sea is slashing,
It is going wild.
The angry sea is thrashing,
The blue waves are frightening.
The water is fierce,
The sea is extra wavy,
It's dark blue,
It's turquoise and white.
The sea is angry,
I can hear the waves crashing,
I can hear the seagulls squawking.
The water is smashing,
The water is whooshing,
And the sea is ferocious.

Ben Pugh (9)
St Martin Of Porres RC Primary School

THE SEA

The sea is rough like a lion, very fierce.
In the sea fish swim gently through the colourful bright water.
The stones crunching under your feet.
The sea is a very cold place when the day is cold.
It's salty and sometimes dirty.
But the sea will always be the sea.

Frank Robinson (8)
St Martin Of Porres RC Primary School

THE SILENT, DEADLY LEOPARD

The leopard sways his hips,
His glossy coat shining in the morning sun.
Sleekly he wanders,
Looking for prey,
When suddenly,
He bares his teeth.

He leaps across the day ground,
Faster and faster,
His eyes fixed on his prey,
His large teeth at the ready,
But . . .

His prey escapes,
And everything's silent.
He turns and begins to make his way back,
The silent, deadly leopard.

Imogen Massey (11)
St Martin Of Porres RC Primary School

THE MAGICAL WORLD OF THE SEA

Little fish swim under the sea,
Come on, come on and listen to me.
All the mermaids comb their hair.
All the mermen watch and stare,
Then they go back under the sea.
They party until there's no one there.
So come on, come on and listen to me.

Natalie O'Brien (9)
St Martin Of Porres RC Primary School

THE SEA

In the sea there are lots of fish,
We eat them off our dish.
Sometimes it's calm sometimes it's rough.
Watch the wonderful waves flowing.
Back and forth, back and forth.
It might be soft it might be wild.
I like it when it's warm but not when it's freezing.
In the sea the shells are patterned.
The sea is like a big blue paradise.
There are lots of fish that live in the sea.
The sea, oh the sea!

Antony Aguirre (8)
St Martin Of Porres RC Primary School

THE ROARING SEA

The sea, oh how it roared that night as we sailed over the sea.
It crashed that night on the rocks and scared us stiff.
It boiled, oh such a noise it made that night.
It shook and threatened to tip us over.
Oh how it shook us about when we crossed the unknown sea.
It swelled all night and day.
Then when at last the morning came it relaxed
And the ship sailed gently on the waves.
Oh to think of those days it makes me sick.

Luke McGowan (8)
St Martin Of Porres RC Primary School

THE LONELY TREE

The poor lonely tree,
Standing alone.
His green veiny friends, have gone
They lie on the floor
In every shade and colour,
Orange, yellow, gold,
Pink, red, beige,
White, brown, green.
They're smooth, they're rough.
The colours clash together
Lying in a clutter
As if they couldn't care.
The last one's gone.
It's floating in the air.
The rain starts to pour.
Damp, wet leaves everywhere,
The poor lonely tree starts to cry.
Oh don't cry your leaves are back
It's summer.

Christina Paul (10)
St Martin Of Porres RC Primary School

THE SEA

The sea is rough and turquoise,
It's angry and mad.
It is howling at night and calm in the morning.
The sea is gleaming, it is blue, white and different colours.
Under the sun the sea is silver but at night it is glowing under the moon.
The waves are like dolphins jumping out of the ocean.

Joshua Baptiste (9)
St Martin Of Porres RC Primary School

UNDER THE SEA

Under the sea, come with me
The blue waves slashing on the shore.
I just couldn't ask for more!
Under the sea, sea, sea
Come with me, me, me!
Ebb and flow, watch and go.
That's the way the world goes round!
Under the sea, with my friends I go!
Under the sea come with me!
Crabs and fishes are all around.
Under the sea do come with me!

Elizabeth Camara (9)
St Martin Of Porres RC Primary School

SAD!

I am lost,
I am sad,
I am alone,
In the biggest toy shop in the world.
I don't like being alone,
I start to sob,
I am isolated, desolated,
I start to wail,
I am miserable and upset,
But finally my parents find me,
And we are happy again.

Carl Bleach (10)
St Martin Of Porres RC Primary School

I FEEL ALONE

I feel alone,
Deserted,
In a world of my own,
Not a friend in the world,
It seems that I'm alone wherever I go,
Everyone hates me only me.
My friends deserted me long ago,
In the playground I sit alone,
On my own,
I try to play,
But it's like they push me away.
At home I'm alone,
A miserable person.
Who no one wants to play with.
I stare through the glass
It's like it's isolating me in a box.
No one can hear me,
I'm not there anymore.
I feel alone,
Deserted,
In a world of my own.

Emma Holtom (10)
St Martin Of Porres RC Primary School

I WAS LOST AND ALONE

I was lost and alone
I was little and I was very sad.
My cousins at the time
Wouldn't let me play with them
Or even let me play their games.
I had no brother or sister
I was alone at parties
And I was alone at celebrations.
My mum and dad found out about this
So they then gave me a brother.
When I was six
I had a brother called Pascal.
I was happy and I was pleased.
Then the greatest thing in my life happened.
I met Oliver and we became close friends
And we still are.
I then met some children and we talked.
I am now eleven
The children are now my best friends.
Even my cousins are now playing with me
And letting me join their games.
I now know that I will never be lost or alone again.

Daniel Rassaby (11)
St Martin Of Porres RC Primary School

ALONE

I feel all alone in the dark,
When all you can see is the park,
When I was cold, someone told,
I had to go home in a lark.

I feel somewhat mellow,
When all I want to do is bellow!
I looked at my friend,
He said I was round the bend.
I felt like I wanted to depart.

I felt quite tearful that night,
When I saw somebody fight.
I left them alone, for I was at home
And I walked into the beautiful night.

Sean Hamill (10)
St Martin Of Porres RC Primary School

ALONE IN A FORTRESS

I am alone in the dark deserted fortress wailing for company.
But the only company I have is my echo
And the cold winter breeze whistling and cracking.
I dropped to the cold, icy floor, cold and lifeless.
Then I heard the warm voices of children playing heartily
So I ran out and felt ecstatic to have lots of company around me.

Sean Daly (10)
St Martin Of Porres RC Primary School

FEELING ALONE

I'm alone in my bedroom
I feel wretched
I think of people who are alone
I try to hold back my waterfall,
Tearful tears in my eyes
I can't, I cry.

I fall to the ground with grief
I feel desolated in my own home.
My tears stopped falling
But I still felt mellow inside
Someone calls me, but who
I wipe away the tear marks.

Sinead Whitney (11)
St Martin Of Porres RC Primary School

CAT

I know a cub that is soft and furry
But also very scary.
He's got a mum who is queen of the grounds.
His sisters and brothers have deadly claws
And they are very good at their chores.
But if you see Dad, you are dead meat
For the rest of the family.
Do you know why?
He has blood-dripping teeth,
And his claws are sharp as compass points.
He runs like Road Runner, so if you are like me
Never go too near that family.

Christina Donellan (11)
St Martin Of Porres RC Primary School

MY HANDS

Are very soft and rough.
They can be good,
They can be bad,
But my hands are my friends.
Hands are good to us.
Me and my hands get on all right
And I love my hands and I think you like yours too.
My hands carry things round.

Danielle O'Neill (8)
St Martin Of Porres RC Primary School